ORCHIDS

by
FLOYD S. SHUTTLEWORTH
HERBERT S. ZIM
and GORDON W. DILLON

Revised by
ALEC M. PRIDGEON

Illustrated by
ELMER W. SMITH

GOLDEN PRESS • NEW YORK
Western Publishing Company, Inc.
Racine, Wisconsin

Orchids are a large, worldwide, exciting family of higher plants that deserve attention beyond the casual glamour long associated with them. The beauty of wild species and elegance of cultivated hybrids are widely acclaimed. But orchids are a unique, highly evolved plant group of great scientific importance as well. Further, they are relatively hardy and can be grown, studied, and enjoyed by any interested amateur.

This book surveys the great orchid family as it illustrates and describes those selected wild forms that best show the family's characteristics and diversity. It also attempts to show those species most commonly cultivated and used in breeding.

This book exists because of the fine cooperation of the Orchid Herbarium of Oakes Ames, Harvard University, and the American Orchid Society. Thanks must go to Elmer Smith for his painstaking research and precise art, and to James Hathway for editorial assistance. We want to express our appreciation to Leslie Garay, Paul Mangelsdorf, Charles Schweinfurth, Fred Fuchs, Calaway Dodson, Taylor Alexander, and Jerry L. Strohm for their many valuable suggestions and for the use of their materials.

F.S.
H.S.Z.
G.D.

CONTENTS

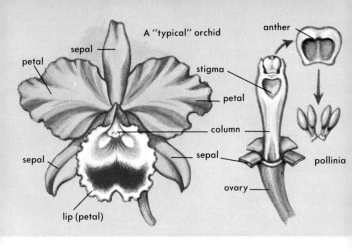

A "typical" orchid

anther

sepal

petal

stigma

petal

column

sepal

sepal

pollinia

ovary

lip (petal)

WHAT IS AN ORCHID?

The orchid family is perhaps the largest family of flowering plants. Over 25,000 species have been described, and equally as many hybrids have been produced by crossing wild and cultivated forms. Orchids range from plants only a fraction of an inch high with flowers about the size of pinheads to some with 5–10 foot stems whose flower stalks are 15 feet long.

These widely diverse plants are all deemed orchids because of their flower structure. All orchid flowers have 3 sepals (outer whorl) and 3 petals (inner whorl), although some of these parts may be fused or reduced. One of the petals (the lip or labellum) is different from the others, often larger and more showy. Usually the flower grows so that the highly variable lip is the lowest segment. Projecting from the center of the flower is the fleshy, club-shaped column, a fusion of the male (staminate) and female (pistillate) reproductive organs. This feature, above all others, characterizes an orchid. At the top (apex) of the column is the anther, with its pollen grains grouped in 2—8 masses, called pollinia. Immediately below the anther is the female portion of the column, the stigma—a sticky, depressed surface on which the pollinia are deposited during pollination. Below the stigma is the ovary which, after fertilization, expands into a seed capsule. A single orchid capsule or pod may contain a million seeds, each about as fine as face powder. Propagation of orchids from seed is not easy.

Orchids belong to the monocots, seed plants with a single seed leaf (cotyledon), parallel leaf veins, and flower parts in threes. They are related in the broad sense to lilies, bananas, palms, and grasses.

TWO MAIN ORCHID GROUPS based on growth patterns are shown below. Sympodial orchids (left), such as cattleyas and dendrobiums, have a main stem or axis that stops growing at the end of each season. A new lead then grows from the rhizome, developing its own pseudobulb (thickened, bulblike stem) and its own inflorescence. Monopodial orchids (right), such as vandas and phalaenopsis, have a main stem that grows steadily year after year, producing flower stalks from the axils of the leaves.

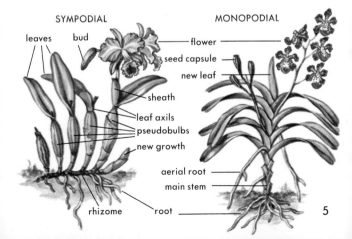

SYMPODIAL

MONOPODIAL

leaves
bud
leaf axils
pseudobulbs
new growth
flower
seed capsule
new leaf
sheath
aerial root
main stem
rhizome
root

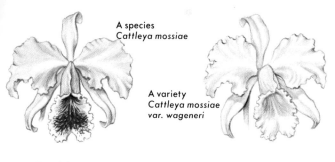

A species
Cattleya mossiae

A variety
*Cattleya mossiae
var. wageneri*

CLASSIFICATION of the orchid family is not yet final. In the Dressler system (1981) the family *Orchidaceae* is divided into 6 subfamilies, over 725 genera, and approximately 25,000 species. This book describes 413 species of 166 genera. The organization follows that of the first edition, although current concepts of evolutionary advancement in orchids now differ.

Closely related orchids, often those with similar vegetative features, are placed in the same or allied groups. Orchids of the same species usually look like one another, the flowers varying chiefly in size or color. Within genera, differences are more marked. Orchids of the same subtribe share some characteristics, but are likely to show more differences than similarities.

According to the botanical system for naming plants, orchids are given a basic name of two units—a genus (pl. genera) and a species name. Thus, *Oncidium papilio* refers to only one specific kind of orchid. The first name—*Oncidium*—indicates that this orchid belongs to the genus *Oncidium*, a large group of almost 500 species. (All the scientific names are Latin or Latinized.) To indicate minor differences in size, color, shape or growth, some orchids receive an additional varietal name. Thus, we have *Cattleya mossiae var. wageneri*.

A cultivar
Cattleya mossiae
'Linden's Champion'

A species cross
Cattleya mossiae
X C. warscewiczii

Few horticultural varieties are illustrated in this book, but you will see many at orchid shows. The names of such cultivars are printed in roman type enclosed within single quotes after the italicized Latin names of species (*Cattleya mossiae* 'Linden's Champion'). A small x between the generic and specific epithets indicates a hybrid (*Calanthe x veitchii*). A large X between the names of two species (*Cattleya mossiae X Cattleya warscewiczii*), two hybrids, or a species and a hybrid designates a horticultural cross (p. 10).

HORTICULTURAL FORMS.

Both amateurs and commercial growers develop new hybrids, name them when they bloom, and register the names. Thereafter, all plants originating from that cross or other crosses between the same parents bear that same hybrid or "grex" name. There are definite procedures that must be followed to register a cross officially. Originally, the registrars were the British orchid firm of Sanders Ltd. Registration now is done by the Royal Horticultural Society in England, and all new names are printed in the English journal *The Orchid Review*. To register a new orchid hybrid, an application form must be filled out, stating genus and proposed name of the hybrid, along with parentage of the cross. Application must be by the originator or with his permission. Other data required include the date of the making of the cross, the date of the first flowering, and description of the first flowers. If it is approved, it appears in *The Orchid Review*. A compilation of such registrations is published every five years, called *Sanders' List of Orchid Hybrids*. Computerization of the list will facilitate reference and new entries.

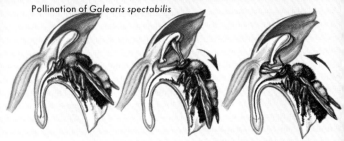

Pollination of *Galearis spectabilis*

Bee enters orchid   picks up pollinia   deposits pollinia on stigma or another orchid

POLLINATION. Orchid flowers have so developed that cross-pollination is normally necessary. Insects are usually the pollinators but birds are involved in some species. Many orchids require a particular kind of insect as pollinator. The flowers are so intricately constructed that the insect is forced into contact with the pollinia, which it carries to another flower and deposits, involuntarily, on the stigmatic surface of that flower.

Male bees are responsible for the pollination of many genera of orchids, such as *Orchis, Catasetum, Cycnoches, Gongora*, and others. A metallic-colored bee, *Euglossa hemichlora*, lands on a lip of *Gongora grossa*, loses its hold on the waxy surface and falls downward, sliding on its back on the curved surface of the column. As it passes

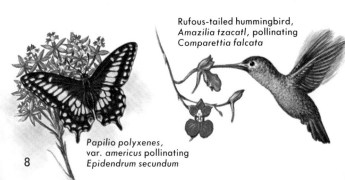

Rufous-tailed hummingbird, *Amazilia tzacatl*, pollinating *Comparettia falcata*

Papilio polyxenes, var. *americus* pollinating *Epidendrum secundum*

8

the male part of the flower, it picks up the pollinia on its abdomen. When it enters another flower of *Gongora grossa*, the bee deposits the pollen masses on the stigma of the column.

Butterflies and moths also may be pollinators. The bright-rose *Epidendrum secundum* is pollinated by a butterfly attracted by nectar. Moths usually pollinate white or light-colored flowers which emit strong odors at night. For a story of a moth that probably pollinates *Angraecum sesquipedale*, see p. 152. Among species pollinated by hummingbirds are *Laelia milleri*, *Elleanthus capitatus*, and *Comparettia falcata*. Flies and mosquitoes pollinate some orchid flowers. About 3% of orchid species self-pollinate with some adaptive device which causes the stalk of the pollinia to grow and curve downward, forcing the pollinia against the stigma.

In the production of hybrids, commercial growers and amateurs transfer pollinia to the stigma of a flower. Pollinia can be obtained by carefully removing the anther cap with the tip of a toothpick. Pollinia will stick to the toothpick and can be transferred directly to the stigmatic surface. A brush is useful.

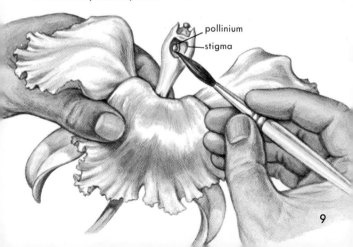

pollinium

stigma

9

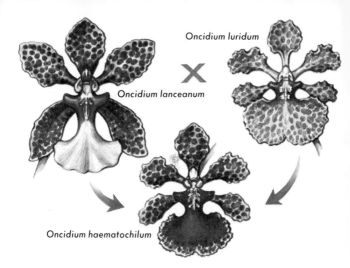

Oncidium luridum

X

Oncidium lanceanum

Oncidium haematochilum

ORCHID HYBRIDIZATION occurs both naturally and artificially. No other family of plants has produced as many hybrids, either in total numbers or in the number of complex crosses. This genetic fluidity of orchids may be associated with their relatively recent evolution as a distinct plant group. Many natural hybrids exist. When two closely related species grow intermingled in an area, the pollen of one may be transferred to the stigma of the other and sometimes a hybrid is formed. This natural hybrid may breed true, producing offspring that resemble their parent plants, and thus become established as a new species. Many species have probably arisen in this manner. *Oncidium haematochilum* is thought to be a natural hybrid between *Oncidium lanceanum* and *Oncidium luridum*. *Cattleya guatemalensis* arose as a natural cross between the orange-flowered *Cattleya aurantiaca* and the purple-flowered *Cattleya skinneri*. This cross has been repeated artificially.

Over a period of many years, natural hybrids may cross back with either or both parents and thus produce all kinds of intermediate forms. Such hybrid "swarms," as they are called, make it difficult to determine the natural variation of the species.

Intergeneric crosses—crosses between species in different genera—are much less common in nature but are very common among the artificially produced orchid hybrids. An outstanding example of a natural intergeneric hybrid is *Laeliocattleya elegans*.

Although some native species of orchids are grown commercially, the majority of commercial plants are artificially produced hybrids. The many *Cattleya* hybrids are usually the result of numerous successive crosses involving a large number of species, each of which has contributed some desirable characteristic to the ultimate offspring. Crosses between *Laelia* and *Cattleya* (known as *Laeliocattleya* and commonly abbreviated as *Lc.*) and between *Cattleya* and *Brassavola* (called *Brassocattleya*, abbreviated as *Bc.*) are very numerous. However, to get the large fringed lip of *Brassavola*, the brilliance of the lip of *Laelia*, and the size and shape of *Cattleya*, trigeneric crosses involving all three genera are made and are known as *Brassolaeliocattleya* (*Blc.*).

Laeliocattleya elegans

This hybrid arose as a cross between *Laelia purpurata* and *Cattleya leopoldii*. Many named varieties of this natural hybrid grow wild in parts of Brazil.

11

A Show Exhibit of Cattleyas

With over 100,000 hybrids already named and registered, the possibilities of new hybrids are still virtually unlimited. Even among the showy corsage types such as *Cattleya, Cymbidium,* and *Vanda,* much remains to be done. And with the non-corsage types such as *Oncidium, Lycaste, Epidendrum, Phalaenopsis,* and others, the amateurs, followed by the commercial growers, have made many interesting crosses and will make many more in the future.

When crosses are made, consideration is usually given to different species in the same genus, or at least between species of genera in the same subtribe. However, crosses have been made successfully between species of genera belonging to different subtribes. Such a cross is that between species of *Lycaste* and *Bifrenaria.* These crosses indicate that the orchid family is genetically in a fluid state and that our concept of genera and subtribes needs further study.

Although thousands of hybrid orchids have been made, we still do not know very much about the inheritance of specific characteristics. Color may be inherited as a single gene, either as a dominant or a recessive. For example, in *Cattleya*, a yellow is usually a recessive trait and is hidden by the genes for purple with which it is crossed. In *Laelia*, yellow is commonly dominant and masks the purple of the other parent. In some cases color may be due to a number of interacting genes. Undesirable characteristics may be inherited as readily as desirable ones. Only by experiment can the amateur, or the commercial grower, determine how a particular trait is inherited. By his experimentation, the hybridizer, provided that he keeps careful records of his crosses and the results, may add significantly to the knowledge of inheritance in orchids.

Mixed orchids staged in a show as a window greenhouse

American Orchid Society

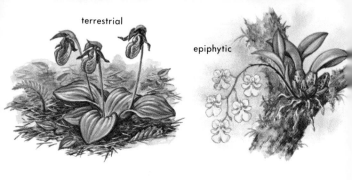

terrestrial

epiphytic

WHERE ORCHIDS GROW

Orchids are found in nearly all parts of the world from the arctic regions to the tropics, although it is in the warmer areas of the earth where they are most plentiful, not only in numbers but also in the great variety of forms. They are found from sea level up to 14,000 feet, but are most common at altitudes between 1,500 and 7,000 feet.

Although many orchids, especially in the arctic and temperate regions, grow in the ground and are thus terrestrial, the majority, in tropical and subtropical areas, grow attached to trees or on rocks and are called epiphytes. No orchids are parasitic, although some of the non-green orchids grow in close association with fungi and are dependent on them for their food.

In the American tropics the greatest variety of orchids are found in the cloud forests where the nights are cool and humidity is high. Often trees are so loaded with orchids, ferns, begonias, bromeliads, gesneriads, and other epiphytes that the branches of trees break under their weight. Most orchids grow in areas where there are wet and dry seasons. Such orchids need an extended dry (rest) period or they do not flower properly. Some genera are limited to certain geographic areas, whereas others are worldwide. The chart at the bottom of the page shows the geographic distribution of 20 prominent genera. Note that the popular corsage genus, *Cattleya,* as well as the related *Laelia* and *Epidendrum,* are limited to the Americas, while *Vanda* and *Dendrobium* are restricted to Asia, the Asiatic Islands, and Australia. The terrestrial *Habenaria* and *Spiranthes* occur worldwide although centers of abundance may be limited.

DISTRIBUTION OF PROMINENT GENERA

GENERA	North America	Central America	South America	Europe	Africa	India	Malaysia	Burma	Philippines	Australia	New Zealand
Bulbophyllum	x	x	x		x	x	x	x	x	x	x
Cattleya	x	x	x								
Coelogyne						x	x	x	x		
Cymbidium					x	x	x	x	x	x	
Cypripedium	x			x		x					
Dendrobium						x	x	x	x	x	x
Epidendrum	x	x	x								
Habenaria	x	x	x	x	x	x	x	x	x	x	
Laelia	x	x	x								
Masdevallia	x	x	x								
Maxillaria	x	x	x								
Odontoglossum	x	x	x								
Oncidium	x	x	x								
Paphiopedilum						x	x	x	x		
Phalaenopsis						x	x	x	x	x	
Pleurothallis	x	x	x								
Spathoglottis						x	x	x	x	x	
Spiranthes	x	x	x	x		x	x	x	x	x	x
Vanda						x	x	x	x	x	
Vanilla	x	x	x		x	x	x	x	x		

HABITATS of orchids vary from dry sandy areas to bogs and aquatic habitats, from shady temperate forests to tree tops in cloud forests. Some species are restricted in their habitats, being confined to a particular environment, but others are found over a wide range. In tropical forests, most orchids grow on high limbs of trees where there is an abundance of light and air. They may not be visible from the ground, but careful examination of a single felled tree may reveal up to 50 different species.

BOGS AND WET MEADOWS are often the home of certain terrestrials such as *Cypripedium, Habenaria, Spiranthes,* and *Calopogon.* These can stand a drying-out period but need considerable moisture to grow.

SHADY WOODS of the temperate areas yield a number of terrestrial forms which grow in the rich humus. These include the Rattlesnake Plaintain, *Goodyera,* and some of the non-green orchids such as *Hexalectris* and *Corallorhiza.*

SAND DUNES along the coast of Great Britain and the northern and western European seaboard are the home of *Epipactis dunensis* or Dune Helleborine. Its deep-seated rootstock penetrates the compact sandhills built up around dwarf willow bushes.

ROCKS are also a substrate upon which many orchids can grow. Even rock walls may hold lithophytes, as such species are called. In Brazil, *Cattleya elongata* forms large patches on exposed rock. See pp. 59-60.

MANGROVE SWAMPS which receive the full force of salt sprays contain a number of epiphytic species which can withstand the desiccating effect of salt. *Encyclia boothiana* grows thus in the Florida Keys.

UNDERGROUND would not seem a likely place for orchids but several subterranean species are known, all occurring in Australia. Lacking chlorophyll, they grow with aid of a fungus and even flower beneath the surface of the soil. See p. 28.

TREES are the habitats of most epiphytic orchids in tropic and subtropic areas. The majority of orchids grow in this manner, their whole existence spent high in the air with their roots closely clinging to the trees' branches.

GRASS AREAS, offering little shade, may contain such handsome orchids as *Platanthera ciliaris, Orchis mascula,* or even the reed-type *Epidendrum ibaguense,* which is supported in tall grass.

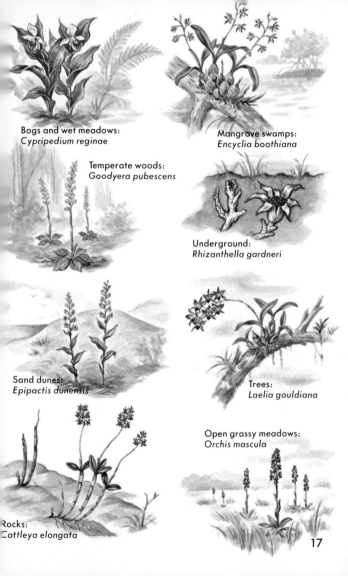

Bogs and wet meadows:
Cypripedium reginae

Mangrove swamps:
Encyclia boothiana

Temperate woods:
Goodyera pubescens

Underground:
Rhizanthella gardneri

Sand dunes:
Epipactis dunensis

Trees:
Laelia gouldiana

Open grassy meadows:
Orchis mascula

Rocks:
Cattleya elongata

17

Information on orchids can be found in scores of books published in many parts of the world. Some deal only with orchids from a particular region; others are more general. Many deal with orchids in cultivation. A few references are listed below.

Arditti, J. [ed.]. *Orchid Biology: Reviews and Perspectives*, volumes 1-4. Cornell University Press, Ithaca, New York, 1977-1987. Definitive treatments on all scientific aspects of orchids.

Bechtel, H., P. Cribb, and E. Launert. *The Manual of Cultivated Orchid Species*. MIT Press, Cambridge, Massachusetts, 1981. A standard reference work.

Dressler, R. L. *The Orchids: Natural History and Classification*. Harvard University Press, Cambridge, Massachusetts, 1981. One of the most detailed and respected classifications and discussions of the orchid family.

Dunsterville, G. C. K., and L. A. Garay. *Venezuelan Orchids Illustrated*. Andre Deutsch, London, 1959-1976. One of the most complete orchid floras ever compiled.

Hawkes, A. D. *Encyclopedia of Cultivated Orchids*. Faber and Faber, London, 1965. The most comprehensive listing of orchid species around the world.

Luer, C. A. *Native Orchids of Florida*. 1972. *Native Orchids of the United States and Canada*. 1975. New York Botanical Garden, New York. The most up-to-date, best illustrated treatments of their kind.

Northen, R. T. *Home Orchid Growing*. Van Nostrand Reinhold, New York, 1970. A standard work that every orchid grower and fancier should have.

Sheehan, T. and M. *Orchid Genera Illustrated*. Cornell University Press, Ithaca, New York, 1979. Sixty-one exquisite pages of watercolors showing the most commonly grown orchid genera accompany detailed descriptions and culture of each.

CLUBS AND ORGANIZATIONS can be a source of

much valuable information and help. There are more than 490 orchid societies in the United States and throughout the world. Membership is helpful to beginning amateurs. Informative journals are published by some, such as the American Orchid Society (see p. 156) whose Yearbook lists addresses of other organizations. Societies in all parts of the world welcome members from other countries. Another source of information is the commercial grower who is willing to help.

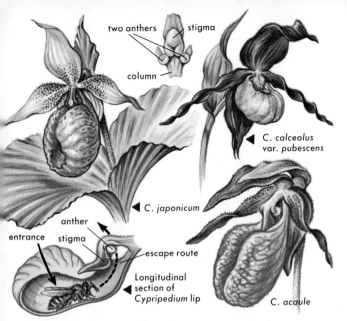

two anthers — stigma

column

◄ C. calceolus var. pubescens

◄ C. japonicum

anther

entrance stigma

escape route

Longitudinal ◄ section of Cypripedium lip

C. acaule

CYPRIPEDIUM, or Lady's Slipper, is a genus of terrestrial orchids. About 30 species grow in temperate and subtropical regions of the world. They have no pseudobulbs. The plicate foliage arises from an underground rhizome. A dozen species occur in U.S.A.

CYPRIPEDIUM JAPONICUM, from China and Japan, is nearly stemless with two fanlike leaves about 6 in. long. Flower stem is 1 ft. tall, with a flower 3½ in. across.

CYPRIPEDIUM CALCEOLUS, the Yellow Lady's Slipper, grows 2 ft. tall with leafy stems. The 1-2 flowers vary in color and size up to 5 in. across. Var. *pubescens* is native to North America.

CYPRIPEDIUM ACAULE, Pink Lady's Slipper, is usually less than a foot tall with two basal leaves, 8 in. long and 3 in. wide. Solitary flowers are up to 4 in. across.

Blooms April-July in eastern North America from Newfoundland to South Carolina and as far west as Minnesota, often in bogs or moist woods.

19

PHRAGMIPEDIUM, the tropical American Lady's Slipper, with narrow, tufted leaves, is a terrestrial or epiphytic orchid with no pseudobulb. Several flowers may appear in succession on a single stalk. About 20 species occur from southern Mexico to Peru and Brazil. They are often wrongly called *Cypripedium* or *Selenipedium*. *P. caudatum*, found from Mexico to Ecuador and Peru, has leathery, yellow-green leaves up to 2 ft. long and 1½–2 in. wide. Flower stalks, up to 3 ft. tall, have 1–6 large flowers with ribbon-like petals, often nearly 3 ft. long.

P. caudatum

S. chica

SELENIPEDIUM, with 4 tropical American species, is a tall, reedy plant with folded leaves and apical spikes of slipperlike flowers. *S. chica* grows to 15 ft.

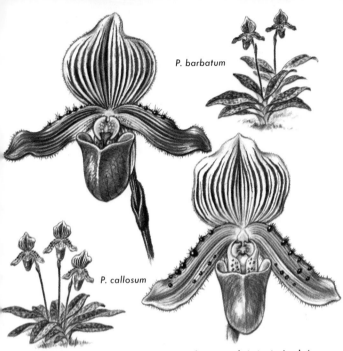

P. barbatum

P. callosum

PAPHIOPEDILUM, the genus of tropical Asiatic Lady's Slippers, includes about 60 species and a large number of horticultural hybrids. Many are grown for the cut flower trade; their large waxy flowers appear almost artificial. Paphiopedilums grow mostly as terrestrials or on rocks; they also lack pseudobulbs. The leathery leaves may be green or mottled.

PAPHIOPEDILUM BARBATUM has tongue-shaped marbled leaves about 6 in. long and 1 in. wide. Solitary flowers, 3-4 in. across, are borne on 10-12 in. stems. Native to S. E. Asia.

PAPHIOPEDILUM CALLOSUM has marbled rigid leaves, 10 in. long and 2 in. wide. The solitary flowers, about 4 in. across, are long-lived and variable in color. Native to S. E. Asia.

PAPHIOPEDILUM INSIGNE, a native of the Himalayas, has narrow, light-green leaves, up to 12 in. long and 1 in. wide. The 4-5 in. flowers are glossy.

PAPHIOPEDILUM HIRSUTISSIMUM, another Himalayan species, has single, very hairy flowers, up to 5½ in. across. The narrow leaves are keeled.

PAPHIOPEDILUM ROTHSCHILDIANUM, found in Borneo, has several 3½-5 in. flowers on a 2-2½ ft. stalk. Its 1-2 ft. leaves are 3 in. wide.

PAPHIOPEDILUM BELLATULUM, a marbled-leaved species from Burma and Thailand, has rounded, spotted 2½-3 in. flowers on very short stems.

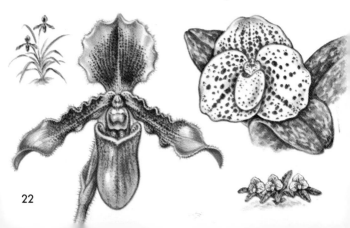

ORCHIS, a genus of terrestrial orchids of Europe, Asia, and North America, has tuberous roots, and mostly basal leaves. The ground roots of two European species, known as salep, make a bland, tapioca-like food. Some species of *Orchis* were transferred to the genera *Galearis* or *Dactylorhiza*.

GALEARIS SPECTABILIS, the Showy Orchis, grows in eastern North America from New Brunswick and Arkansas south to Georgia. Flowers, about 1 in. long, bloom on foot high stalks.

DACTYLORHIZA MACULATA, found in Europe and Asia, grows 18-20 in. high. The lower leaves are spotted with purple. Flower clusters on the 1 ft. spike may be 3½ in. long.

ORCHIS SIMIA, from middle and south Europe, has 2-4 basal leaves clustered around a 1 ft. stem bearing a dense spike of 1¼ in. flowers, each suggestive of a grinning monkey.

23

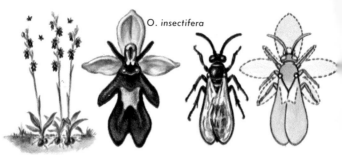

O. insectifera

OPHRYS, with nearly 20 terrestrial species, all under a foot tall, is found in Europe, North Africa, and Western Asia. *Ophrys* has tapered leaves and a spike with a few straggly flowers. Flowers have a metallic color, are hairy, and resemble insects. *O. insectifera* has a lip that resembles the female *Argogorytes mystaceus*. A male wasp, attempting copulation, picks up pollinia. *O. speculum* has a lip like the female *Campsomeris* with head toward column. Male insect enters flower head first. *O. lutea* has a lip that resembles female *Andrena* with head toward apex of lip. Male insect reverses position. Pollination is by pseudocopulation.

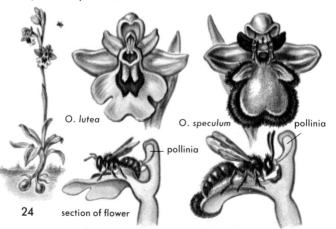

O. lutea

O. speculum

pollinia

pollinia

section of flower

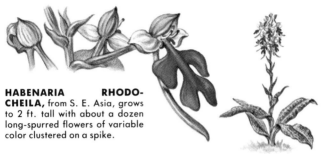

HABENARIA RHODO-CHEILA, from S. E. Asia, grows to 2 ft. tall with about a dozen long-spurred flowers of variable color clustered on a spike.

HABENARIA, the Rein Orchid, is a large group (about 500 species) of tuberous-rooted terrestrials found widely in the East Indies, Africa, Europe, and North and South America. Many grow in bogs of moist acid soil. Flowers vary in size and color; many have a fringed lip; all are spurred at the base. Related to *Platanthera*.

PLATANTHERA CILIARIS, the Yellow-fringed Orchid, is a wide-ranging, hardy orchid of eastern N.A. It grows to 3½ ft. tall and has a terminal spike of bright-yellow or orange flowers, to 1 in. across.

HABENARIA SUSANNAE, from India, China, and Malaysia, grow 1½-3 ft. tall with fragrant, 3-4 in., white flowers. Lip is three-lobed, the two outer lobes fringed, the center lobe tonguelike. A very beautiful species.

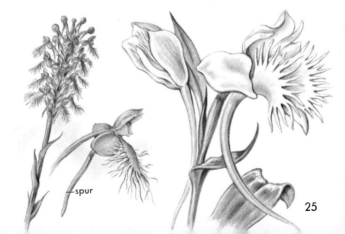

—spur

DISA, a genus of about 130 species of terrestrial orchids in South and East Africa, Madagascar, and nearby islands, has flowers in a wide variety of colors. During late summer (January and February), some disas make quite a show in the eastern Transvaal region of South Africa. The dorsal sepal is usually erect, hooded, and spurred. Petals and lip generally are inconspicuous.

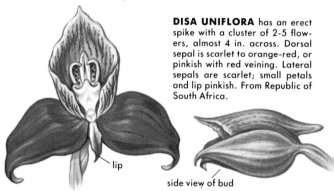

DISA UNIFLORA has an erect spike with a cluster of 2-5 flowers, almost 4 in. across. Dorsal sepal is scarlet to orange-red, or pinkish with red veining. Lateral sepals are scarlet; small petals and lip pinkish. From Republic of South Africa.

lip

side view of bud

HERSCHELIANTHE SPATHULATA has 1-4 flowers, each about an inch across. The upper sepal is greenish, shaded with violet; the prominent lip has a very long claw. Common name is "Old Man with a Pipe."

HERSCHELIANTHE GRAMINIFOLIA is a tuberous-rooted species with azure-blue flowers. The lip is light blue or white, edged with dark blue. Leaves, narrow and grasslike, do not appear until after the 2 in. flowers are gone.

lip

AUSTRALIA and nearby islands have so many native orchids that they are often taken for granted. Species are extremely variable in size and shape; some are fragrant; a few have an unpleasant odor. Most are small-flowered. Included among the distinctive orchids of Australia are a number of the dendrobiums (pp. 73–81) and the terrestrial genera shown below and on p. 28.

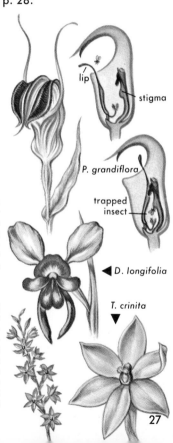

PTEROSTYLIS, with over 70 species, ranges from New Guinea to New Zealand and Australia. Its sensitive lip acts as a trapdoor. Gnats and mosquitoes, attracted by nectar at base of the lip, are trapped when the lip springs shut. Escaping through a tunnel, the insect picks up pollinia which it later carries to another flower. About 20 minutes later the trapdoor opens. *P. grandiflora,* most attractive of the Greenhoods, has a single 1½ in. flower on a leafy stem. It is from eastern Australia.

lip

stigma

P. grandiflora

trapped insect

DIURIS (more than 40 species in Australia) is known as the Donkey Orchid. These terrestrials have grasslike leaves and flowers with two ear-like petals. *Diuris longifolia,* the Common Donkey Orchid, has 3–5, variable, 1½ in. flowers.

◀ *D. longifolia*

THELYMITRA, the Sun Orchid, includes numerous terrestrial species in New Zealand, New Caledonia, Java, the Philippines, and Australia. Their variously colored flowers, all with hooded, winged columns, open only in strong sunshine. *Thelymitra crinita,* the Queen Orchid, has broad leaves. Its stems may reach 3 ft. with 7–17, light-blue, 1½ in. flowers.

T. crinita

▼

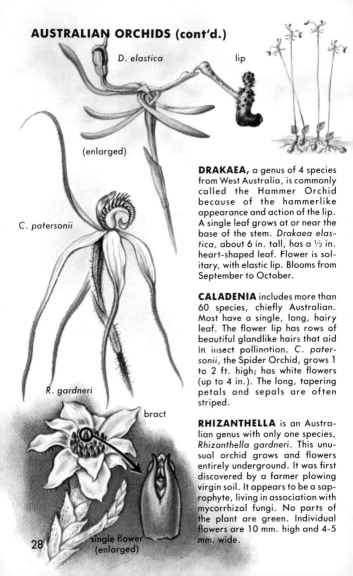

AUSTRALIAN ORCHIDS (cont'd.)

D. elastica

lip

(enlarged)

C. patersonii

R. gardneri

bract

single flower
(enlarged)

DRAKAEA, a genus of 4 species from West Australia, is commonly called the Hammer Orchid because of the hammerlike appearance and action of the lip. A single leaf grows at or near the base of the stem. *Drakaea elastica,* about 6 in. tall, has a ½ in. heart-shaped leaf. Flower is solitary, with elastic lip. Blooms from September to October.

CALADENIA includes more than 60 species, chiefly Australian. Most have a single, long, hairy leaf. The flower lip has rows of beautiful glandlike hairs that aid in insect pollination. *C. patersonii,* the Spider Orchid, grows 1 to 2 ft. high; has white flowers (up to 4 in.). The long, tapering petals and sepals are often striped.

RHIZANTHELLA is an Australian genus with only one species, *Rhizanthella gardneri.* This unusual orchid grows and flowers entirely underground. It was first discovered by a farmer plowing virgin soil. It appears to be a saprophyte, living in association with mycorrhizal fungi. No parts of the plant are green. Individual flowers are 10 mm. high and 4-5 mm. wide.

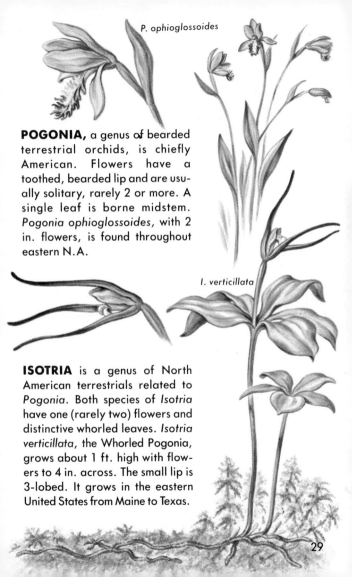

P. ophioglossoides

POGONIA, a genus of bearded terrestrial orchids, is chiefly American. Flowers have a toothed, bearded lip and are usually solitary, rarely 2 or more. A single leaf is borne midstem. *Pogonia ophioglossoides,* with 2 in. flowers, is found throughout eastern N.A.

I. verticillata

ISOTRIA is a genus of North American terrestrials related to *Pogonia.* Both species of *Isotria* have one (rarely two) flowers and distinctive whorled leaves. *Isotria verticillata,* the Whorled Pogonia, grows about 1 ft. high with flowers to 4 in. across. The small lip is 3-lobed. It grows in the eastern United States from Maine to Texas.

29

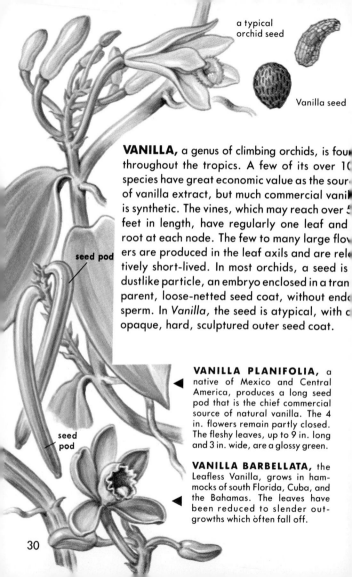

a typical
orchid seed

Vanilla seed

VANILLA, a genus of climbing orchids, is fou[n]
throughout the tropics. A few of its over 10[0]
species have great economic value as the sour[ce]
of vanilla extract, but much commercial vani[lla]
is synthetic. The vines, which may reach over 5[0]
feet in length, have regularly one leaf and [a]
root at each node. The few to many large flo[w]ers are produced in the leaf axils and are rel[a]tively short-lived. In most orchids, a seed is [a]
dustlike particle, an embryo enclosed in a tran[s]parent, loose-netted seed coat, without endo[o]sperm. In *Vanilla,* the seed is atypical, with [a]
opaque, hard, sculptured outer seed coat.

VANILLA PLANIFOLIA, a
native of Mexico and Central
America, produces a long seed
pod that is the chief commercial
source of natural vanilla. The 4
in. flowers remain partly closed.
The fleshy leaves, up to 9 in. long
and 3 in. wide, are a glossy green.

VANILLA BARBELLATA, the
Leafless Vanilla, grows in hammocks of south Florida, Cuba, and
the Bahamas. The leaves have
been reduced to slender outgrowths which often fall off.

seed pod

seed
pod

30

ELLEANTHUS is a genus of tropical American orchids either terrestrial or epiphytic. The strong-veined leaves resemble *Sobralia*, but the less than ½ in. flowers are clustered in close heads, with bract behind each flower. *Elleanthus aurantiacus,* found from Costa Rica to Peru, grows 3 ft. or more tall with distinctive bunched branching.

lip

E. aurantiacus

bract

SOBRALIA is a genus that is terrestrial or epiphytic and native to tropical America. Stems are reedlike with strong-veined alternate leaves. Flowers are solitary or clustered, usually large and showy, but most last only one day. New blooms are produced over a long period.

SOBRALIA CANDIDA, of Venezuela and Peru, grows to 20 in. tall. Narrow leaves drop off except 2 or 3 at the top of the stem which bears a single 2 in., short-stalked flower, white with red spots on lip.

SOBRALIA MACRANTHA, from Central America, grows to 8 ft. tall. Flowers, varying from 6-10 in. across, are usually produced singly over a long period. A pure white form is known.

B. striata

BLETILLA is a genus of 9 terrestrial species native to China, Japan, and Taiwan. Although often called *Bletia,* it is not closely related to that genus. *Bletilla striata* is a commonly cultivated species. Flowers, 1–2 in. across, open in succession. A hardy orchid of temperate regions.

CALOPOGON, with grasslike leaves, is a genus of North American terrestrials, common in swamps or bogs. *Calopogon tuberosus,* found from SE Canada to the Bahamas and Cuba, has a conspicuous yellow-bearded lip. Flowers are 1–1½ in. across. *Calopogon pallidus,* the Pale Grass-Pink, has 1 in., rose-pink to white flowers produced in succession over a long flowering season.

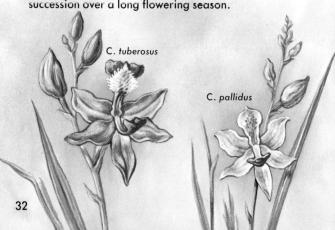

C. tuberosus

C. pallidus

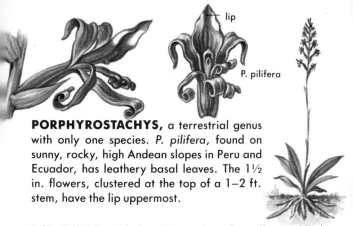

PORPHYROSTACHYS, a terrestrial genus with only one species. *P. pilifera*, found on sunny, rocky, high Andean slopes in Peru and Ecuador, has leathery basal leaves. The 1½ in. flowers, clustered at the top of a 1–2 ft. stem, have the lip uppermost.

PONTHIEVA includes 25 species of small terrestrial orchids with a basal rosette of thin leaves. Roots are fleshy or sometimes fibrous. The erect stalk bears a loose cluster of small flowers with lip uppermost. *P. racemosa*, the Shadow-Witch, has flowers ½ in. across. *P. maculata* occurs from Costa Rica to Venezuela and Ecuador. Its flowers are 1–1¼ in. across.

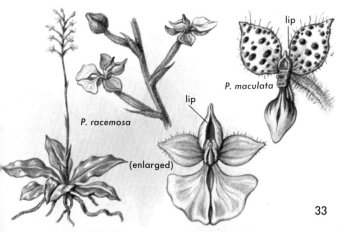

JEWEL ORCHIDS include a group of genera so closely related that species often are indistinctly defined or agreed upon by botanists. They are grown for their colorful foliage rather than for their flowers. Most of the dwarf species are difficult to cultivate but grow well when conditions are right. Culture varies with species.

GOODYERA PUBESCENS, Downy Rattlesnake Plantain, is one of the many species of this terrestrial genus. The dark-green leaves are netted with white and silver. White ¼ in. flowers grow in cylindrical spikes. Found in eastern North America.

ANOECTOCHILUS ROXBUR- GHII, from the Himalayas, has bronze-green foliage netted with copper and reddish, short-spurred ½ in. flowers. *A. sikkimensis,* also from the Himalayas, has velvety leaves from deep green to dark red, veins copper.

DOSSINIA MARMORATA is a native of Borneo, with dark velvety green leaves shaded with orange-brown and lines of gold. The 5 in. spike has many white ¼ in. spurless flowers.

LUDISIA DISCOLOR is a variable species from India, Indo-China, and Indonesia, with dark-purple or dark-green leaves and red or gold veins. Its small (¾ in.) flowers are white.

ZEUXINE STRATEUMATICA (below) is a member of a genus which may or may not have variegated leaves. This particular Asian species does not. It was probably introduced to the United States with the importa- tion of centipede grass seed and is spreading rapidly throughout Florida and the Gulf States. It commonly comes up as a "weed" in cultivated places. Flowers are less than ½ in. across, borne on dense spikes.

▼

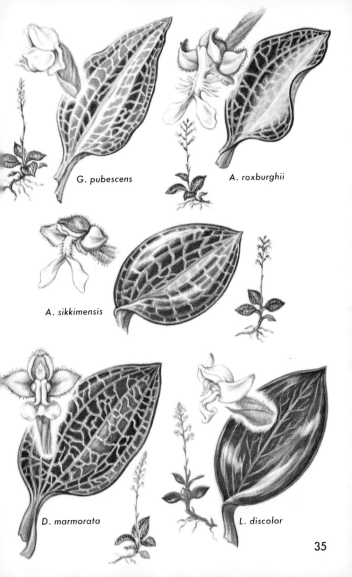

G. pubescens

A. roxburghii

A. sikkimensis

D. marmorata

L. discolor

35

SPIRANTHES CINNABAR-INA, the Scarlet Ladies' Tresses, grows in highlands of Texas, Mexico, and Guatemala. Leaves are up to 10 in. long and stems, with tubular 1 in. flowers, up to 3 ft. tall.

SPIRANTHES is a widely distributed terrestrial genus that grows in woods and grasslands from the Arctic almost to the Antarctic regions. Plants are often narrow-leaved with spirals of small flowers in terminal spikes. Many are tuberous-rooted. This group, with over 300 species, is often divided into a number of genera.

SPIRANTHES CERNUA, Nodding Ladies' Tresses, grows from Nova Scotia to Florida, New Mexico, and Utah. Its common name comes from the more or less nodding position of the ¼ in. flowers on the spike.

SPIRANTHES AURANTIACA, common in Mexico and Guatemala, has many hairs covering the stem above the uppermost leaf. The flowers, about 1 in. long, vary from orange to orange-red.

STELIS CILIARIS has stems clustered. The solitary leaf is narrow and fleshy. Flowers are less than ½ in. in diameter; sepals, maroon to purplish, are hairy on their margins.

STELIS is a large group of more than 500 epiphytic species found in tropical America. The small flowers have sepals larger than the petals. Many plants are miniatures, less than 1 in. high; others grow to 9 in. Racemes emerge from the base of the leaf.

MASDEVALLIA, a large genus of about 350 tropical American species, is usually epiphytic. The beautifully colored or oddly shaped flowers are produced singly, or occasionally on short racemes. The basally united sepals are the most conspicuous parts of the flowers. Many species transferred to *Dracula*.

MASDEVALLIA CAUDATA, with flowers 1 to 1½ in. across, has lateral sepals extending into tails up to 3 in. long. Lip and petals are small. It grows in the Andes of Colombia.

DRACULA CHIMAERA produces one flower (4-8 in. across) at a time but produces them in succession. The large hairy sepals have tails to 7 in. long. A number of named varieties exist.

MASDEVALLIA COCCINEA, a variable, 2-3 in., one-flowered species, ranges from light rose-pink to magenta purple; often blood crimson. Dorsal sepal has a long tail. Native of Colombia.

37

PLEUROTHALLIS, a very large genus of perhaps 2,000 tropical American species of epiphytic orchids, includes plants smaller than a thimble to some over 2 ft. high. Flowers are produced singly or in racemes from the axil of the leaves. One species occurs in Florida.

PLEUROTHALLIS INSIGNIS, with plants 1 ft. tall, has two or three red-streaked yellowish flowers, ½ in. long. It is a native of Venezuela.

PLEUROTHALLIS GROBYI, only 3 to 4 in. high, has several green to yellow ¼ in. flowers streaked with crimson. It is from Central and South America.

PLEUROTHALLIS TALPI-NARIA, from northern South America, is up to 8 in. tall, with a solitary ¾ in. flower borne on each of several stalks fascicled in large spathe.

S. pulvinare

SCAPHOSEPALUM is closely related to *Masdevallia* (p. 37), but the lateral sepals and lip, normally the lowest part of the flower, are uppermost. Small flowers are produced in succession. About 25 species occur in the American tropics. *S. pulvinare* has medium-sized (1 in. long) flowers with short-tailed, purple sepals.

LEPANTHOPSIS, a genus of about 25 tropical American species, has flowers arranged in two rows. *L. vinacea,* endemic to Venezuela, has leaf and stem 2½ in. tall. Many ⅛ in. flowers open on a bracted stem arising from base of the leaf.

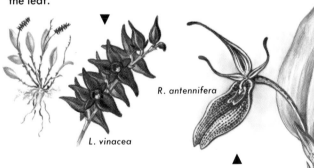

R. antennifera

L. vinacea

RESTREPIA usually produces single flowers, larger and of brighter colors than *Pleurothallis* (p. 38). The upper sepal and petals are threadlike, the lower sepals larger and joined. *Restrepia antennifera,* of Colombia, has 2½ in. yellowish flowers, marked with red or purple.

39

L. elata

LIPARIS, the Twayblade, is a cosmopolitan genus of 250 species of chiefly terrestrial orchids. Pseudobulbs are small to almost lacking. Most have small, often dull-colored flowers in terminal racemes. Several species occur in the United States. *Liparis elata* grows from Florida and Mexico southward to Brazil and Peru. Flowers have a large purple lip and are nearly ½ in. across.

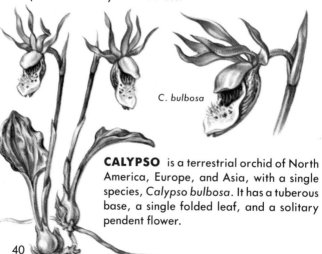

C. bulbosa

CALYPSO is a terrestrial orchid of North America, Europe, and Asia, with a single species, *Calypso bulbosa*. It has a tuberous base, a single folded leaf, and a solitary pendent flower.

COELOGYNE, a genus of 120 species of epiphytic and terrestrial orchids from the Eastern Hemisphere, has pseudobulbs with 1 or 2 leaves and a raceme of showy flowers. Inflorescences are usually produced from the center of young growths.

COELOGYNE FLACCIDA, from the cool Himalayas, will bloom in warmer climates. The arching spike has 5 to 12 heavily scented, 1½ in. whitish flowers. The 3-lobed lip is marked with red and yellow.

COELOGYNE PANDURATA has pseudobulbs set widely apart on a straggly rhizome. Sometimes called the Black Orchid, it has 5 to 15 pale-green 3-4 in. flowers with a fiddle-shaped, greenish-yellow and black lip.

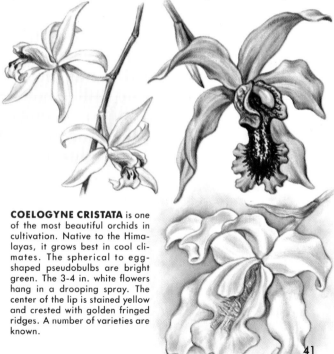

COELOGYNE CRISTATA is one of the most beautiful orchids in cultivation. Native to the Himalayas, it grows best in cool climates. The spherical to egg-shaped pseudobulbs are bright green. The 3-4 in. white flowers hang in a drooping spray. The center of the lip is stained yellow and crested with golden fringed ridges. A number of varieties are known.

41

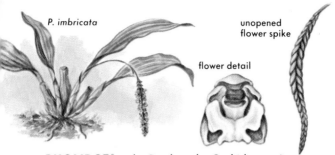

P. imbricata

unopened
flower spike

flower detail

PHOLIDOTA, the Rattlesnake Orchid, gets its common name from the resemblance of the bracts of the unopened flower spike to the rattles of a rattlesnake. Species grow in India, China, and various places throughout the Pacific. *Pholidota imbricata* has small insignificant flowers, ⅓ in. across.

PLEIONE has large attractive flowers produced singly or in pairs on short stems growing from the base of the annual pseudobulbs. The single leaf falls as the bulb matures. The 14 species occur in China, Taiwan, the Himalayas, and Southeast Asia.

PLEIONE PRAECOX has flowers about 3 in. across. Sepals and petals are slender and rose-purple to pink. The lip is trumpet-shaped and fringed. Grows best in cool, high places. *Pleione praecox* has flask-shaped, wrinkled pseudobulbs of light green mottled with brown. Flowers appear in the fall.

pseudo-bulb

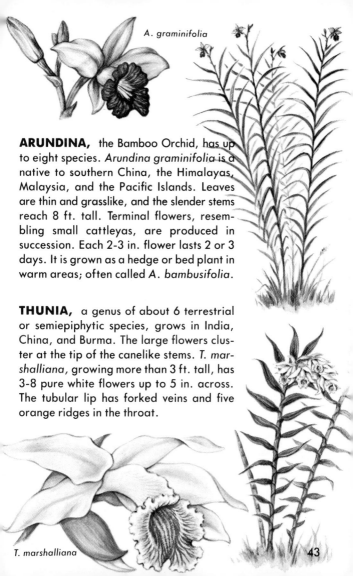

A. graminifolia

ARUNDINA, the Bamboo Orchid, has up to eight species. *Arundina graminifolia* is a native to southern China, the Himalayas, Malaysia, and the Pacific Islands. Leaves are thin and grasslike, and the slender stems reach 8 ft. tall. Terminal flowers, resembling small cattleyas, are produced in succession. Each 2-3 in. flower lasts 2 or 3 days. It is grown as a hedge or bed plant in warm areas; often called *A. bambusifolia*.

THUNIA, a genus of about 6 terrestrial or semiepiphytic species, grows in India, China, and Burma. The large flowers cluster at the tip of the canelike stems. *T. marshalliana*, growing more than 3 ft. tall, has 3-8 pure white flowers up to 5 in. across. The tubular lip has forked veins and five orange ridges in the throat.

T. marshalliana

43

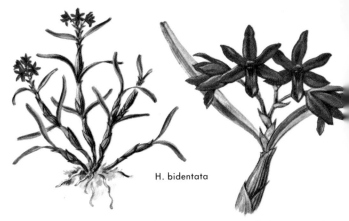

H. bidentata

HEXISEA, a tropical American genus of 6 species, is related to *Epidendrum* but differs in vegetative growth and in structure of the flowers. Flowers are borne in short racemes. Pseudobulbs are branched or grow one on top of the other. *Hexisea bidentata,* the most commonly grown species, has bright-red flowers.

LEPTOTES, another relative of *Epidendrum,* is a genus of 3 or 4 dwarf species from Brazil, Argentina, and Paraguay. Pseudobulbs are short and the single leaves are fleshy. *Leptotes bicolor* has 1½ in. white flowers with a rose lip. Sepals and petals are similar.

L. bicolor

EPIDENDRUM is a large genus with hundreds of species found from North Carolina to Argentina. Most are epiphytic although some grow on rocks or in the soil. This group of orchids shows great variation in plant form and in the size of the flowers. Flowers are few to many and are usually borne on a terminal raceme. A very few species have racemes arising laterally from the base of the pseudobulbs.

From the nature of the plant growth, two major groups of species are recognizable. One group has definite, and often prominent, pseudobulbs with one or at most a few leathery leaves at the top (pp. 46-48). The other group are reed-type epidendrums without pseudobulbs. In a few instances the base of some reed-like stems may be enlarged.

Through the years many species of *Epidendrum* have been moved to other genera (e.g. *Barkeria, Encyclia*) as taxonomists uncovered relationships among certain species groups. This always creates confusion at first, but in the long run improves our knowledge.

Encyclia boothiana   *Barkeria lindleyana*   *Epidendrum anceps*

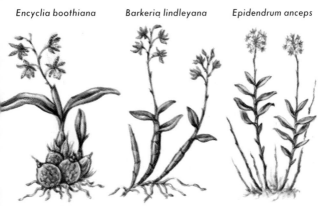

45

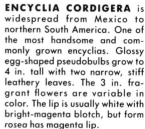

var. *roseum*

ENCYCLIA CORDIGERA is widespread from Mexico to northern South America. One of the most handsome and commonly grown encyclias. Glossy egg-shaped pseudobulbs grow to 4 in. tall with two narrow, stiff leathery leaves. The 3 in. fragrant flowers are variable in color. The lip is usually white with bright-magenta blotch, but form *rosea* has magenta lip.

ENCYCLIA TAMPENSIS, a native of south Florida and the Bahamas, has pseudobulbs and long sprays of variably colored flowers up to 1½ in. across. Generally sepals and petals are greenish yellow to tan and the lip is white with a purple blotch. Some forms are variously marked.

ENCYCLIA ALATA, common from Mexico to Costa Rica, also has egg-shaped pseudobulbs with 2 or 3 leaves. Flowers are numerous, variable in size, usually yellowish green marked with purple. This lip is 3-lobed; side lobes are widely separated from the center lobe.

ENCYCLIA ADENOCAULA is a Mexican species, well worthy of cultivation. Egg-shaped pseudobulbs have 2 or 3 leaves. The branching raceme is 2 to 3 ft. tall, with many 3-4 in. rose-mauve flowers. Minute warts cover peduncle, pedicels, and ovaries.

ENCYCLIA FRAGRANS, common from Mexico and the West Indies to northern South America, has variable pseudobulbs, usually somewhat flattened, and typically with 1 leaf. The fragrant 2 in. flowers are creamy white, with a purple-striped shell-shaped lip usually uppermost. Related species are *Encyclia radiata* and *Encyclia chacaoensis*.

ENCYCLIA COCHLEATA, ranging from Florida to Brazil, has flattened, clustered pear-shaped pseudobulbs with 2 or 3 light-green, somewhat thin leaves. Known in England as the Cockleshell Orchid, it was the first epiphytic orchid to flower there (in 1787). Size varies, to 3 in. in some Mexican forms.

ENCYCLIA VITELLINA has a limited range in Mexico and Central America. It grows at high altitudes and requires cooler weather than most encyclias. Has oval pseudobulbs 1 to 3 in. high and 3 sprays of 10 to 15 orange-red flowers, each about 1½ in. across.

ENCYCLIA POLYBULBON, widespread from Mexico to Honduras and in Cuba and Jamaica, has 1 in. pseudobulbs on creeping rhizomes. Usually only one flower about ¾ in. across nestles between the two leaves. Flowers vary in size; leaves differ in shapes and size.

47

EPIDENDRUM CILIARE, found from Mexico to Brazil and in the West Indies, has stout foot-tall stems. Spidery flowers are borne in clusters of 3 to 7 and may reach 5 in. across. The 3-lobed lip is white with tonguelike center lobe 1 to 2 in. long. The two side lobes are fringed.

EPIDENDRUM PRISMATO-CARPUM has stout tapering pseudobulbs, 5-6 in. high. The erect racemes bear 10-15 creamy-yellow 2 in. flowers, blotched with purple spots. The ovary is three-sided, hence the name.

EPIDENDRUM PARKINSON-IANUM grows hanging down with small pseudobulbs bearing a single, thick, hard, flat, sickle-shape leaf. The 1 to 3 greenish-white flowers are 4 in. or more across. The lip is three-lobed. The species *falcatum* is less robust, with smaller flowers.

EPIDENDRUM STAMFORD-IANUM, common from Mexico to northern South America, has stout spindle-shaped pseudo-bulbs with 2 thick leaves. Unlike nearly all other epidendrums, the inflorescence arises laterally from the base of the pseudobulb although occasionally one may arise terminally. The showy 1½ in. flowers are greenish yellow, with purplish-red spottings.

THE GENERIC NAME *Epidendrum* comes from the Greek meaning "upon a tree," referring to the epiphytic habit of the plants. In Europe, early botanists were not familiar with epiphytes and all epiphytic orchids were called epidendrums. Linnaeus, in *Species Plantarum* (Ed. 1, 1753), included in *Epidendrum* species now considered to be in *Arachnis*, *Brassavola*, *Cymbidium*, and several other genera.

Most orchids in cultivation are epiphytes but are usually grown in pots or beds. In nature, epiphytic orchids grow on high branches of trees and collecting them can be a hazardous adventure.

Elmer W. Smith

BARKERIA SKINNERI, a reed-type plant once considered an *Epidendrum*, has slender stems about 1 ft. tall. Fifteen to 30 deep-rose flowers, each over 1 in. across, cover most of the inflorescence. It grows in Guatemala and is closely related to *B. lindleyana* pictured on p. 45.

EPIDENDRUM STENOPETALUM, also having reed-type (usually spindle-shaped) stems, is found from Mexico and Jamaica to South America. Its showy 1 in., rose to pink, very flat flowers have winglike lobes on the tip of the column.

49

EPIDENDRUM IBAGUENSE, usually called *E. radicans*, is a terrestrial reed-type orchid that grows in dense, prostrate, and twining masses. The 1-1½ in. orange-yellow to red flowers are clustered in head-like racemes. It is widespread from Mexico to South America. In warm climates it is often planted in beds in full sun.

EPIDENDRUM PSEUDEPI-DENDRUM is a Central American reed-type orchid growing 2-3 ft. tall. Inflorescences are terminal, with 1-3 flowers 2½ in. across. The narrow sepals and petals are bright green with an orange-scarlet lip, appearing like wax or plastic.

EPIDENDRUM SCHUMAN-NIANUM, a beautiful epiphytic reed-type orchid, grows high in the trees of the rain forests of Panama and Costa Rica. Stems, 3 ft. or more long, are hairy and spotted. The inflorescences are branched, with many small (¾ in.) flowers. In direct sunlight the sprays are strikingly vivid and colorful.

EPIDENDRUM NOCTUR-NUM grows in Florida, the West Indies, and throughout tropical America. Stems up to 3 ft. tall, usually shorter, are leafy above. The 3-4 in. white flowers are fragrant at night. The center lobe of the lip is long and tonguelike.

EPIDENDRUM SCHLECHTER-IANUM has closely crowded growths sheathed by several small fleshy, green-channeled leaves. The ½ in., almost translucent, greenish-yellow flowers are slightly tinged with pink. One or two grow at the stem tips surrounded by leaves. Native from Mexico to northern South America.

EPIDENDRUM CORONA-TUM, a tall, reed-type epiphyte with terminal, pendent inflorescence, grows from Guatemala to Trinidad and in S. America. The few to many, 2 in., fleshy flowers have a 3-lobed lip that appears 4-lobed because the mid-lobe is cleft.

EPIDENDRUM CONOPSEUM has short, leafy stems, less than 1 ft. tall. The ½ in., yellow-green flowers are sometimes suffused with purple. This epiphytic orchid grows from North Carolina to southern Florida, in the Gulf States, and in Mexico. At present it is the only epiphytic orchid known to grow anywhere in the United States outside of Florida.

EPIDENDRUM DIFFORME, widespread from southern Florida and Mexico to northern South America, has leafy stems up to 20 in. tall. Flowers are white, yellowish, or greenish. A variable species first introduced in England in 1793.

THREE SHOWY SMALL-FLOWERED ORCHIDS are among those closely related to the epidendrums and cattleyas. These genera, each with only a few species, have small, attractive flowers. West Indian in distribution, these orchids are not widespread, but are commonly found in many orchid collections.

BROUGHTONIA includes one, possibly two, species of epiphytic orchids which grow in Jamaica. The clustered, often overlapping, flattened pseudobulbs have two thick leaves. *B. sanguinea* has up to twelve 1-1½ in. flowers, magenta in color. A yellow form is known.

B. sanguinea

L. domingensis

LAELIOPSIS, a genus with two species, is a West Indian orchid similar to *Broughtonia. L. domingensis* has flowers 2 in. across, blush rose with vivid rose lips, in a 2 ft. branched inflorescence.

N. monophylla

NEOCOGNIAUXIA, a genus with only two species, from Hispaniola, Cuba, and Jamaica, was originally included in genus *Laelia. N. monophylla* has a single leaf and a 2 in., orange-scarlet flower.

CATTLEYA, queen of the orchids, grows epiphytically, sometimes on rocks. The nearly 40 species are tropical American, extending from Mexico to Brazil and Peru. All have prominent pseudobulbs, from 4 in. in height to over three feet tall. Some have only one leaf (unifoliate, pages 53-57) on each pseudobulb while others have two (bifoliate, pages 58-62). With few exceptions, inflorescences arise from the top of mature pseudobulbs and flower buds are normally enclosed in a single or double sheath until shortly before they open. Flower stalks bear one to thirty flowers, depending on the species and the vigor of the plant. In nearly all cases sepals are widely spread and petals are broader than the sepals. The lip is large and showy; its side lobes curve over the column. Cattleyas are the major orchids of commerce. Thousands of hybrids have been produced by crossing *Cattleya* with related genera.

CATTLEYA LABIATA (below), found in 1818, was the first *Cattleya* discovered, in Brazil. The 5 in. flowers vary in color and as many as 5 may grow on a raceme. It blooms in the fall. Most of the cattleyas illustrated on the following two pages are only varieties of this species, but horticulturally are treated as true species. All have one leaf per pseudobulb.

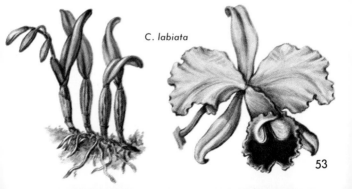

C. labiata

53

UNIFOLIATE CATTLEYAS

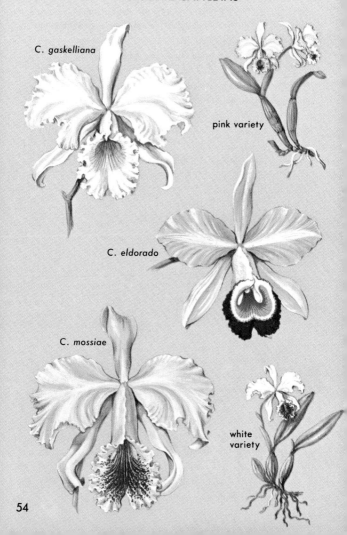

C. gaskelliana

pink variety

C. eldorado

C. mossiae

white variety

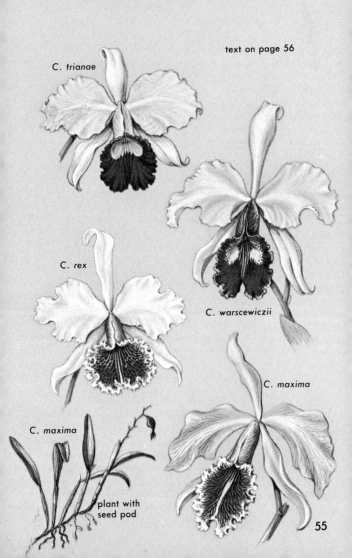

C. trianae

text on page 56

C. warscewiczii

C. rex

C. maxima

C. maxima

plant with
seed pod

55

CATTLEYA GASKELLIANA, a summer bloomer, is highly variable in color, pale amethyst-purple to white. Flowers may reach 7 in. but are usually smaller. A native of Venezuela, this is an easily grown plant.

CATTLEYA ELDORADO, a Brazilian orchid, has pale-lilac to white sepals and petals, with a dark purplish-magenta lip. Blooms in late summer and fall; flowers 4-6 in. across.

CATTLEYA MOSSIAE blooms around Easter or Mother's Day and thus is a popular commercial orchid. There may be 3 to 4 flowers per raceme, and each may reach 6 to 8 in. across. This orchid from Venezuela is a strong grower with handsome flowers.

CATTLEYA MAXIMA, from Ecuador, Colombia, and Peru, has flowers with a striped lip and ruffled mid-lobe.

CATTLEYA TRIANAE, often called Christmas Orchid because it blooms from December to February, comes from Colombia. There are many varieties of this species, varying in color and shape; flowers to 9 in. across.

CATTLEYA REX, from Peru and Colombia, has 4 to 6 in. flowers. In September a single raceme may bear 2 to 7 blooms. This is one of the rarest of the *labiata*-type cattleyas.

CATTLEYA WARSCEWICZII, also called C. *gigas*, has flowers 7 to 11 in. across that open during summer. Flower spikes bear 2 to 7 flowers. Grows in Colombia in sunny locations. Florists feature this flower in June corsages.

CATTLEYA DOWIANA, one of the *labiata* group that is a native of Costa Rica, blooms in late summer. Fragrant flowers reach 8 in. across. A variety, *aurea*, with more gold on the lip, occurs in Colombia and is one of the parents of many yellow *Cattleya* hybrids.

▼

C. dowiana

lip of C. *dowiana* var. *aurea*

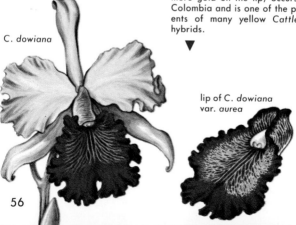

56

CATTLEYA PERCIVALIANA is an ill-scented *Cattleya* with 4 to 5 in. flowers with a deep-orange throat. It comes from Venezuela and flowers in winter, generally around Christmas, but season varies.

CATTLEYA LUTEOLA, found from Brazil to Bolivia, has short, slender pseudobulbs, each with a 3-4 in. leaf. Clusters of 2 in. flowers with or without purple on the lip are produced. Flowers at various times, usually winter.

CATTLEYA LAWRENCEANA from Venezuela and Guyana has more spindly pseudobulbs and leaves often red-tinged. In spring and early summer it produces five or more 4-5 in. flowers, variable in color.

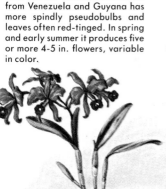

57

BIFOLIATE CATTLEYAS

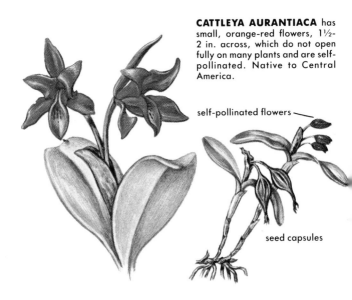

CATTLEYA AURANTIACA has small, orange-red flowers, 1½-2 in. across, which do not open fully on many plants and are self-pollinated. Native to Central America.

self-pollinated flowers —

seed capsules

DEVELOPMENT OF A CATTLEYA SEED CAPSULE

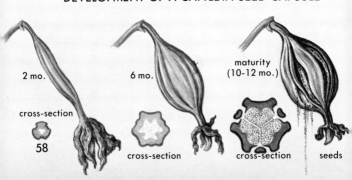

2 mo.

cross-section

6 mo.

cross-section

maturity
(10-12 mo.)

cross-section

seeds

CATTLEYA ACLANDIAE is a small plant with two leaves on each pseudobulb. The 3-4 in. flowers appear in summer. Side lobes do not curve around purple column. Difficult to cultivate.

CATTLEYA BICOLOR, a Brazilian species, has fragrant 4-5 in. flowers. It also has two leaves per pseudobulb. The spadelike lip is dominant in crosses with the *labiata* group (pp. 53-56).

illustrations on page 60-61

CATTLEYA AMETHYSTO-GLOSSA has clusters of 3½-4 in. flowers with spotted sepals and petals. Native to Brazil.

ENCYCLIA (CATTLEYA) CITRINA, a Mexican species, grows hanging down. The flower is sweetly scented.

CATTLEYA BOWRINGIANA, a Central American orchid, blooms in the fall with clusters of up to 20 vivid 2-3 in. flowers.

CATTLEYA ELONGATA, from Brazil, has clusters of variable 3-4 in. flowers on tall stems, atop 1-2 ft. pseudobulbs.

CATTLEYA FORBESII, also from Brazil, has pseudobulbs 12-18 in. tall and 3-4 in. flowers in clusters of 2-5.

CATTLEYA GRANULOSA, another tall Brazilian species, has clusters of five or more fleshy, often spotted flowers, to 4 in.

CATTLEYA GUTTATA, with 4 in. flowers, has several named varieties. The pseudobulbs may be over 4 ft. tall.

CATTLEYA INTERMEDIA has slender, tall pseudobulbs with rose-flushed, 3-5 in. flowers. Native to Brazil, a variety has waxen, pure white flowers.

CATTLEYA SCHILLERIANA with red-tinted pseudobulbs and thick, leathery leaves has shining 4 in. flowers which are fleshy and have purple-brown spots. Often blooms twice a year. Plants are relatively compact with disproportionately large flowers.

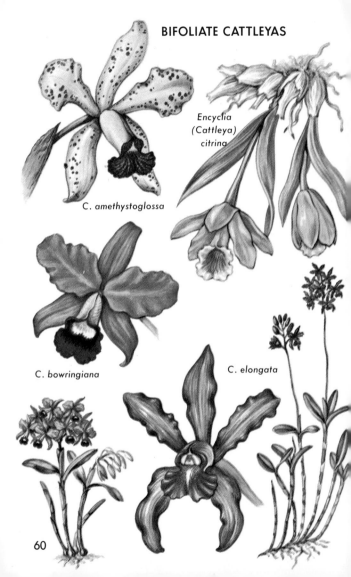

BIFOLIATE CATTLEYAS

C. amethystoglossa

Encyclia
(Cattleya)
citrina

C. bowringiana

C. elongata

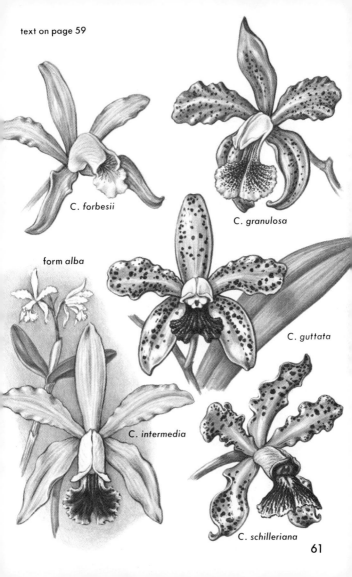

text on page 59

C. forbesii

C. granulosa

form *alba*

C. guttata

C. intermedia

C. schilleriana

CATTLEYA SKINNERI, from Mexico and Central America, resembles C. *bowringiana* (p. 60) but lacks the bulbous bases of the pseudobulbs. In many plants, the 3-5 in. flowers do not fully open. Blooms in early spring but an autumn-flowering variety occurs in Panama.

CATTLEYA VELUTINA has fragrant 4-5 in. flowers with orange-yellow or coppery sepals and petals, spotted with red or purple. The slender erect stems are 18 in. tall. This Brazilian orchid blooms in late summer.

CATTLEYA VIOLACEA, also called C. *superba*, has fragrant, 5 in., flat flowers with deep-rose sepals and petals and a deep-crimson lip. Common from lower altitudes of Peru and northern S.A., this species requires warm temperatures and more water than most cattleyas.

CATTLEYA WALKERIANA differs from most cattleyas in that the 4-5 in. flowers are produced from leafless stems arising from the horizontal rhizome at the base of pseudobulbs, each having one or two leaves.

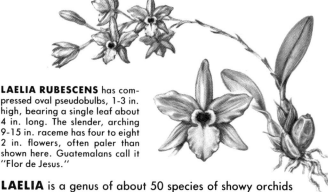

LAELIA RUBESCENS has compressed oval pseudobulbs, 1-3 in. high, bearing a single leaf about 4 in. long. The slender, arching 9-15 in. raceme has four to eight 2 in. flowers, often paler than shown here. Guatemalans call it "Flor de Jesus."

LAELIA is a genus of about 50 species of showy orchids closely related to *Cattleya* and often crossed with it to produce many of our commercial hybrids. Extending from Mexico to South America, these epiphytic orchids reach their highest development in Brazil. Pseudobulbs may be rounded, oval, or greatly elongated. Flowers resemble those of *Cattleya*, but they typically have narrower sepals and a less showy lip.

LAELIA ANCEPS has short, often 4-angled, pseudobulbs with one, sometimes two, leaves. Very variable, with many named forms, the 4 in. flowers are borne 2 to 6 at end of a long scape.

LAELIA FLAVA has cylindrical stems 3-6 in. high with a foot-long raceme of up to 10 medium-sized (2-2½ in.) canary-yellow flowers. A Brazilian species, it blooms in late spring.

cross-section of pseudobulb

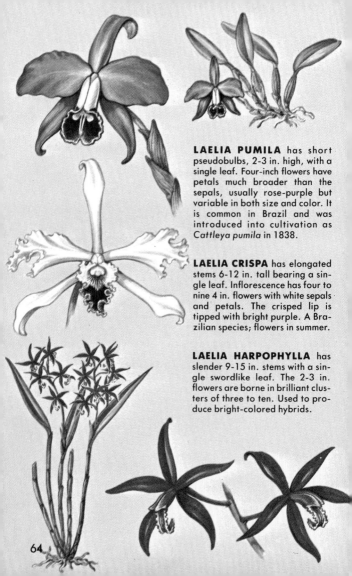

LAELIA PUMILA has short pseudobulbs, 2-3 in. high, with a single leaf. Four-inch flowers have petals much broader than the sepals, usually rose-purple but variable in both size and color. It is common in Brazil and was introduced into cultivation as *Cattleya pumila* in 1838.

LAELIA CRISPA has elongated stems 6-12 in. tall bearing a single leaf. Inflorescence has four to nine 4 in. flowers with white sepals and petals. The crisped lip is tipped with bright purple. A Brazilian species; flowers in summer.

LAELIA HARPOPHYLLA has slender 9-15 in. stems with a single swordlike leaf. The 2-3 in. flowers are borne in brilliant clusters of three to ten. Used to produce bright-colored hybrids.

var. rosea

LAELIA PURPURATA is a beautiful species with 20-30 in. pseudobulbs. The three to nine large flowers are 6-9 in. across and variable in color ranging from white to deep rose-purple. Blooms in summer. A number of named varieties are grown. It is the national flower of Brazil.

LAELIA TENEBROSA has the growth habit of *L. purpurata* but is usually not as tall. The large 7-8 in. flowers are coppery brown with a dusky-purple lip. Flowers in the spring. Frequently used in hybridizing with cattleyas.

LAELIA XANTHINA has slender-stalked pseudobulbs 6-10 in. tall with a single leathery leaf. The two to five clear-yellow, 3 in. flowers have white on the lip with crimson markings. Blooms in spring or early summer.

65

SCHOMBURGKIA is so closely related to *Laelia* that there was at one time considerable discussion about merging the two genera. Extending from Mexico and the West Indies to South America, these vigorous epiphytic orchids are of two kinds; some have two-leaved, spindle-shaped (fusiform) pseudobulbs, others have hollow pseudobulbs with three or more leaves. The upright inflorescence may grow to 6 ft. long.

SCHOMBURGKIA TIBICINIS has hollow pseudobulbs, 12-36 in. long, often inhabited by ants. The inflorescence is 3-6 ft. long with clusters of 3 in. variable flowers, each with narrow, wavy sepals and petals.

SCHOMBURGKIA UNDU-LATA resembles *S. tibicinis* in habit but is usually not quite as tall. Clusters of 2 in., very wavy, purplish-brown flowers resemble bugs as they unfold. The lip is a deep rose-purple.

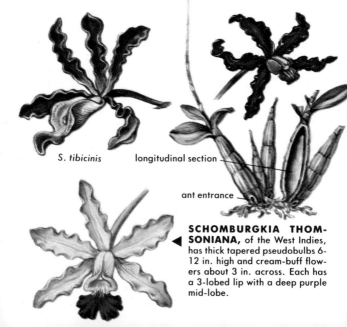

S. tibicinis   longitudinal section

ant entrance

SCHOMBURGKIA THOM-SONIANA, of the West Indies, has thick tapered pseudobulbs 6-12 in. high and cream-buff flowers about 3 in. across. Each has a 3-lobed lip with a deep purple mid-lobe.

BRASSAVOLA is a genus of about 15 tropical American epiphytic orchids with white or greenish-white flowers. Stems are usually small but leaves are leathery and may be short and stubby or long and narrow. Two species, B. digbyana and B. glauca (sometimes separated into the genus Rhyncholaelia), have been used extensively in hybridizing with species of Cattleya and Laelia. Like Laelia, all species have 8 pollinia.

BRASSAVOLA ACAULIS has short, thin pseudobulbs and long rushlike leaves, usually hanging downward. Flowers, 2-3 in. across, have narrow, greenish-white sepals and petals with a whiter, heart-shaped lip.

BRASSAVOLA MARTIANA, found from Brazil to Venezuela, is a species with long, rounded leaves, generally pendent. Three to six, 3-4 in. pale-green flowers with white-fringed lips grow on each raceme.

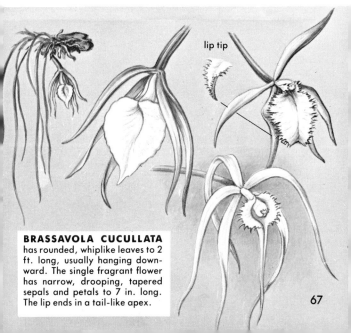

lip tip

BRASSAVOLA CUCULLATA has rounded, whiplike leaves to 2 ft. long, usually hanging downward. The single fragrant flower has narrow, drooping, tapered sepals and petals to 7 in. long. The lip ends in a tail-like apex.

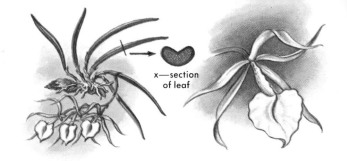

x—section of leaf

BRASSAVOLA NODOSA, Lady-of-the-Night Orchid, varies in size of plants and flowers. Fleshy leaves, grooved on one side, are less than 1 ft. long, upright. The 3 in. flowers, more fragrant at night, are long-lived and bloom throughout the year.

BRASSAVOLA DIGBYANA has reddish pseudobulbs. Single 4-7 in. flower has large, round, creamy-white, heavily fringed lip. Mexico and Belize. Also referred to as *Rhyncholaelia digbyana*.

BRASSAVOLA CORDATA of the West Indies resembles *B. nodosa* but clustered flowers are more numerous and are smaller (usually less than 2 in. across); leaves longer and narrower. Heart-shaped lip is porcelain white. Flower fragrant at night.

BRASSAVOLA GLAUCA is also known as *Rhyncholaelia glauca*. Flowers are solitary, pale green, 4-5 in. across, heavy textured, lip not fringed. Grows in Mexico, Guatemala, and Honduras.

growth habit of B. glauca

ISABELIA is a Brazilian genus of only one species, *I. virginalis*, a small creeping orchid. Closely set pseudobulbs are clothed with fibrous sheaths and needle-like leaves. The solitary 3/8 in. flowers have a flush of rose or pale purple.

I. virginalis

SOPHRONITIS is a small genus of only six or seven species, all of them dwarf plants; native to Brazil and Paraguay. They are cool-growing orchids and do not grow well in warm climates. Small pseudobulbs bear a single flattish leathery leaf and the entire plant is seldom over 3 in. tall. Each of their 1 to 3 flowers is ½ to 3 in. across. Have been used in crosses with *Cattleya* and allied genera to get red shades.

SOPHRONITIS COCCINEA, often called *S. grandiflora*, has 1½-3 in. flowers with brilliant-scarlet sepals and petals, and orange-yellow on the lip. Flowers vary in size and color.

SOPHRONITIS CERNUA has a creeping rhizome with pseudo-bulbs and leaves 1½-2 in. high, flowers up to 1 in. across; cinnabar-red to orange. From warmer climates than *S. coccinea*.

69

SIX SMALL-FLOWERED GENERA shown here are curiosities worthy of including in any orchid collection.

CAULARTHRON, formerly named *Diacrium*, is a genus of two variable species of the West Indies and tropical America. All have thick, usually hollow pseudobulbs. Flowers resemble those of *Epidendrum*, but lip is *not* parallel to the column. In some plants flowers are self-fertilizing and seldom open wide. *C. bicornutum* has clusters of up to 20 white flowers, 1½-2½ in. across.

ISOCHILUS has slender, erect, leafy stems. At the top is a cluster of small brightly colored flowers. *I. linearis*, from tropical America, grows to 24 in. tall with narrow ⅛ in. leaves 2-2½ in. long. Pink to orange to magenta flowers do not open widely.

ARPOPHYLLUM, with fleshy stems and a leathery narrow leaf, is found from Mexico to Colombia. A dense cylindrical raceme of closely set flowers is produced. *A. spicatum* has ¼ in. flowers. In wet areas, leaves are thinner and broader in cross section than in dry areas (below).

COELIA, a genus of five species, includes four once placed in the genus *Bothriochilus*. The epiphytic plants of *Coelia* have swollen pseudobulbs, each with several leaves. Inflorescences develop from the base of pseudobulbs. *C. triptera* is native to Mexico, Guatemala, and West Indies. *C. macrostachya*, from Mexico and Central America, has a raceme of pink or rose-colored flowers, each less than 1 in. long.

SCAPHYGLOTTIS, a genus of about 40 species ranging from the West Indies and Mexico to Brazil, has very small flowers and often a peculiar habit of growth. Spindle-shaped pseudobulbs are often borne on top of one another. *S. violacea* has purple or pink flowers less than ⅛ in. across.

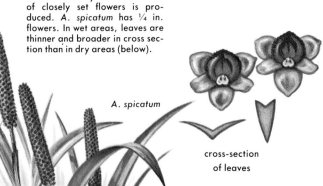

A. spicatum

cross-section
of leaves

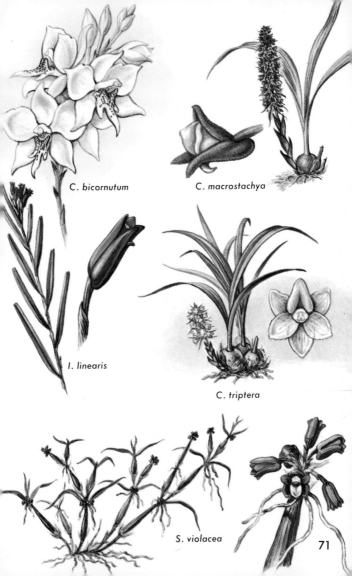

C. bicornutum

C. macrostachya

I. linearis

C. triptera

S. violacea

71

ERIA, found throughout tropical Asia and Polynesia, is a genus of more than 550 species. Flowers are borne singly or in short lateral spikes from the base or the top of the pseudobulbs. Inflorescences are often hairy and may have large conspicuous bracts. Flowers are usually small, up to 2 in. across. There is a great diversity in size and in the persistence of the leaves.

ERIA RHODOPTERA has cylindrical pseudobulbs up to 5 in. tall. The two or three leathery leaves are longer. The raceme, with yellowish or whitish bracts, has many ½ in. flowers in the spring.

ERIA VESTITA, called the Furred Eria, is covered with red-brown hairs on the leaves and pendent racemes. Flowers do not open widely; sepals are nearly 1 in. long. This species grows throughout Malaysia.

bract

bract

ERIA SPICATA, an epiphyte commonly known as *E. convallarioides*, the Lily-of-the-Valley Orchid, has pseudobulbs to 8 in. tall with 3 or 4 thick, leathery leaves. The ½ in., white or straw-colored flowers are densely set in a 3-6 in. spike.

DENDROBIUM, a genus of over 1,400 species, is found from India to Southeast Asia eastward to the Fiji Islands and south to New Zealand. Although some have inconspicuous flowers, others include some of the showiest of orchids. Stems may be pseudobulbous or reedlike, ranging from less than two inches high to over 15 ft. tall. In some, the leaves are evergreen, persisting for several growing seasons; in others, they are deciduous, often falling from the plant just before flowering. Flowers are produced in short or long racemes. All have the lateral sepals united at the base to form a short sac or mentum. Flowers vary from less than ½ in. across to over 4 in. All species are considered epiphytic, although a few grow on rocks or even occasionally in the ground. In many species, small plantlets, called *keikis,* form on old pseudobulbs. When they produce good roots and the second season's growth, they may be removed and potted as separate plants. Numerous hybrids of *Dendrobium* have been made.

DENDROBIUM CHRYSOTOXUM has stout pseudobulbs 6-12 in. tall. The apical spikes have 7 to 15 waxy, golden flowers about 2 in. across. The fringed lip has a darker-orange disc. To bloom well *D. chrysotoxum* requires a long rest.

DENDROBIUM FARMERI, with strongly 4-angled pseudobulbs up to 12 in. long, has a drooping densely packed raceme of apple-blossom pink or white blooms, 2 in. across, each with a hairy yellow lip. Flowers last one to two weeks.

cross-section
of pseudobulb

DENDROBIUM DENSIFLO-RUM resembles *D. farmeri* (p.73) with its 4-angled pseudobulbs 12 in. or more tall. It has a drooping raceme of 2 in. flowers, variably yellow and hairy but not fringed. The 3-4 leaves are persistent.

DENDROBIUM NOBILE, a popular deciduous *Dendrobium*, has many named varieties. Stems grow erect 12 to 24 in. tall with groups of 2 to 3 flowers (about 3 in. across) at each joint or node. Used in hybridization.

DENDROBIUM APHYLLUM, commonly cultivated as *D. pierardii*, has slender pendent stems up to 3 ft. long, clothed with 2 in. pale-rose flowers produced in 2s or 3s from the nodes. Young plants often form on old stems.

DENDROBIUM PRIMU-LINUM, with flowers 2-3 in. across, similar to *D. aphyllum*, has odor of cowslip (*Primula veris*). Seldom does well under cultivation. The mouth of the yellow lip is much wider than high.

keiki

DENDROBIUM HETEROCAR-PUM (also called *D. aureum*) produces flowers in 2s or 3s from nodes of 9-15 in. stems. Fragrant 2-2½ in. flowers have amber to cream sepals and petals. Found from India to Philippines.

DENDROBIUM TRANSPAR-ENS has slender, erect or pendulous stems with 1 in. flowers in pairs from the nodes. It is a native of India and Nepal. A well-flowered plant is attractive, but the species is not widely cultivated.

DENDROBIUM FALCONERI has knotty, branched. pendent stems, 2-3 ft. long. Solitary 2-4½ in. flowers are very showy, the white sepals and petals tipped with purple, white lip with maroon spot and orange blotch.

DENDROBIUM ANOSMUM, usually called *D. superbum*, has 2-4 ft. pendent stems, soon losing their leaves. Flowers, 3-4 in. across, are produced singly or in pairs at nodes of the stems. Odor powerful, but pleasant.

DENDROBIUM FIMBRIA-TUM, a species from Nepal to Malaya, has stems 2-4 ft. tall. From 3 to 15 flowers cluster on the upper, drooping portion of the stem. Blooms are 2-3 in. across, deep orange in color with a fringed lip. The variety *oculatum*, with maroon blotches at base of lip, is most commonly grown.

DENDROBIUM PARISHII has short, uneven, curved stems up to 20 in. long. Flowers, 2-3 in. across, grow from nodes and have the scent of rhubarb.

DENDROBIUM MOSCHA-TUM has 4-6 ft. stems, each with 8 to 15 short-lived flowers, 3-4 in across. Lip is cup-shaped.

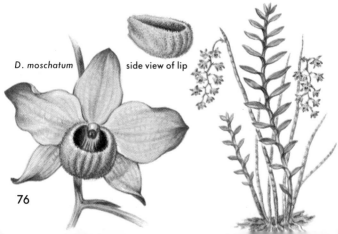

D. moschatum   side view of lip

DENDROBIUM INFUNDIBU-LUM, similar to *D. formosum;* grows at high altitudes and has smaller (to 4 in.) flowers. Sepals and lip form a funnel-shaped spurlike mentum, shown above in a side view of the bud. The species name was derived from this structure (*infundibulum* means funnel in Latin).

DENDROBIUM DEAREI, of the Philippines, has pseudobulbs 1-2 in tall. Leaves persist more than a year. Flowers are 2½ in. across in apical clusters.

DENDROBIUM FORMOSUM, from Nepal to Thailand, has black hairs on its 12-18 in. stems and long-lasting, 4-5 in. flowers.

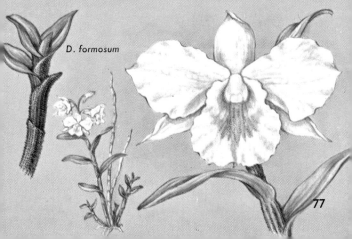

D. formosum

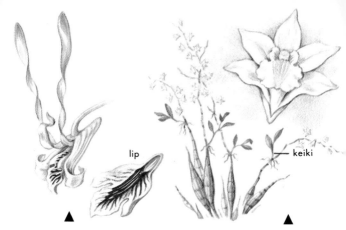

lip

keiki

**DENDROBIUM ANTENNA-
TUM** from New Guinea has stems
2-3 ft. tall with about 10 well-
spaced flowers on a raceme.
Flowers are 2½-3 in. long with
sepals curved backward; erect
petals very narrow and twisted.
Mid-lobe of lip very narrow.

**DENDROBIUM CRUMENA-
TUM,** the Pigeon Orchid, has
pseudobulbs swollen in the middle. About 9 days after a 10°F.
drop in temperature, such as
accompanies a heavy shower, all
affected buds open. Flowers (1-
1½ in.) stay open only a day.

**DENDROBIUM AGGREGA-
TUM** is a dwarf species with clustered 3 in. pseudobulbs, each with
a single leaf. Two-inch flowers, in
hanging clusters, become darker
yellow with age. Closely related
to species on pages 73-74.

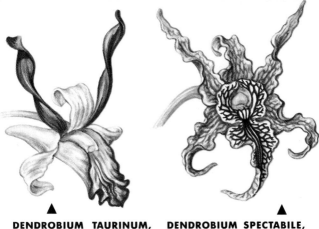

DENDROBIUM TAURINUM, the Bull Orchid, native of the Philippines, has stout, erect stems sometimes 5-6 ft. tall. Inflorescence is 2-4 ft. with 15 to 30 flowers, each 2-2½ in. across. Flower shape and twisted petals resemble bull's head and horns.

DENDROBIUM SPECTABILE, from New Guinea and the Solomon Islands, has 1-2 ft. pseudobulbs and terminal spikes of 5 to 20 flowers. Segments are broad across base and drawn out and twisted. The heavily veined flowers are about 3 in. across.

DENDROBIUM CUCUMERINUM, the Cucumber Orchid from Australia, lacks pseudobulbs. The gherkinlike leaves arise from the stem at short intervals. The flowers are about ½ in. across.

young stem

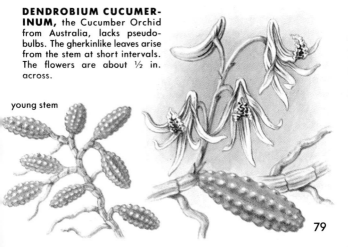

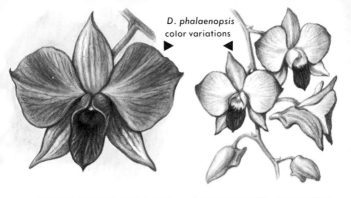

D. phalaenopsis
color variations

DENDROBIUM PHALAEN-OPSIS, an evergreen species with stems 2 ft. or more tall, has long, arching inflorescences. Its few to many, long-lasting, 3-4 in. flowers have wide petals and a painted lip. They may remain in flower 2-3 months. Color varies from deep reddish purple to pure white. This Australian species is used extensively in hybridizing.

DENDROBIUM BIGIBBUM (below left) is similar to *D. phalaenopsis*. It, too, comes from Australia. Center lobe of lip is blunt and notched, not pointed.

DENDROBIUM SUPERBI-ENS, another Australian evergreen orchid, has long, arching racemes with well-spaced 2½-3½ in. flowers. Edges of sepals and petals are wavy. This is a natural hybrid between *D. phalaenopsis* and *D. discolor*.

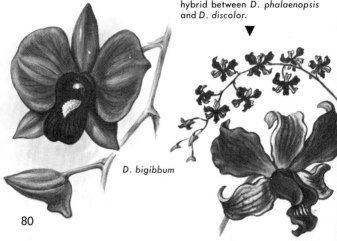

D. bigibbum

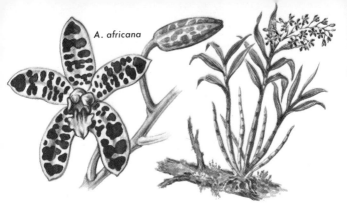

A. africana

ANSELLIA, the African Leopard Orchid, has two variable species. *A. africana*, with cylindrical jointed pseudobulbs up to 2 ft. tall and 4 to 7 plicate leaves, bears many 2½ in. flowers spotted with dark brown.

NEOBENTHAMIA has only a single species, *N. gracilis* (lower left). This tall-growing African terrestrial has glossy leaves and terminal clusters of ¾ in. flowers.

ACROLOPHIA, with 6 species of terrestrials from South Africa, has small flowers. *A. capensis* var. *lamellata* grows 1½ ft. tall with a spray of ¾ in. flowers.

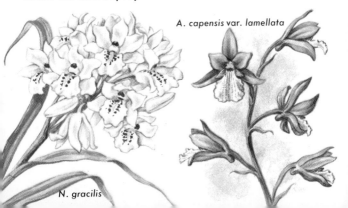

A. capensis var. lamellata

N. gracilis

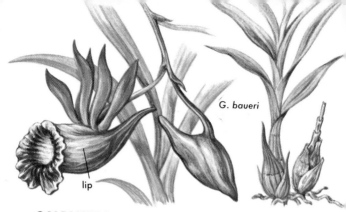

G. baueri

lip

GALEANDRA, a tropical American genus of twenty terrestrial or epiphytic species. Pseudobulbs are covered by leaf sheaths. Leaves are thin and plicate. Inflorescence is terminal. G. baueri has showy 2 in. flowers with funnelshaped lip.

BROMHEADIA, a genus of terrestrial or epiphytic plants, grows from Sumatra to New Guinea. Stems are usually long and slender. Flowers alternate in two rows. B. finlaysoniana, a terrestrial, produces one or two 2-2½ in. short-lived flowers every 10 days or so.

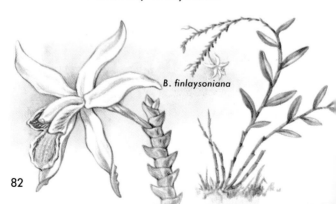

B. finlaysoniana

POLYSTACHYA CONCRETA, formerly *P. luteola,* may be the most widespread orchid known, extending from Florida and the American tropics to African and Asian tropics. The 6 to 12 in. tall epiphytic plant has narrow, lance-shaped leaves and tapering pseudobulbs. Its fragrant, small (¼ in.) greenish-yellow flowers are arranged in loose clusters on an erect, branched inflorescence.

POLYSTACHYA, a genus of nearly 200 species, is found in the tropics, especially in Africa, but also in the Americas and in Asia. Pseudobulbs are small. Inflorescences are terminal with few to many small flowers. Each flower is inverted so that the lip is uppermost. Lateral sepals form a hood over the lip, as shown below.

POLYSTACHYA GRANDIFLORA is an African species with the largest flowers in the genus. The 1 to 3 fleshy flowers are over 1 in. long. Pseudobulbs are 3-4 in. high with leaves as long or longer.

POLYSTACHYA PANICULATA has flattened pseudobulbs which are purplish when young. The panicle is closely set with red-orange ¼ in. flowers, tinged with yellow.

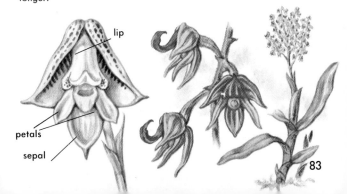

lip

petals

sepal

A. hyemale

APLECTRUM is a North American terrestrial orchid with a single 7 in. leaf arising from the underground corm. The one species, *A. hyemale*, called Putty-root because of gluelike juice derived from corm, has attractive ½ in. flowers extending above the single leaf.

CORALLORHIZA, one of the few orchid genera lacking chlorophyll, includes a dozen species in North and Central America and one species in Eurasia. These terrestrial orchids with coral-like rootstock live on dead organic matter. They all have a leafless stem. *C. maculata*, ranging from Nova Scotia to the Pacific and south to Mexico and Guatemala, has small (½ in.) purplish or yellowish-brown flowers with a spotted white lip.

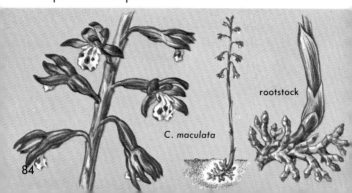

C. maculata

rootstock

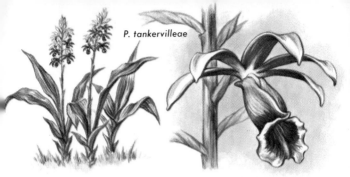

P. tankervilleae

PHAIUS, with about 30 species, ranges from East Africa to tropical Asia and the Pacific Islands. *P. tankervilleae* is known as the "veiled nun" because the petals and sepals of the fragrant flower give it a hooded look. A terrestrial best cultivated in a mixture of loam, peat, and sand.

CALANTHE, a genus of 150 terrestrial species, extends from South Africa and Asia to the Pacific Islands, with a single species in the West Indies and Central America. Parents of the first (1856) horticultural orchid hybrid were calanthes. *C. masuca* is an evergreen species with an erect spike of 2 in. flowers. *C. vestita* has angled pseudobulbs with 18 in. deciduous leaves and a raceme of 2 in. flowers. The genus name is Greek for "beautiful flower."

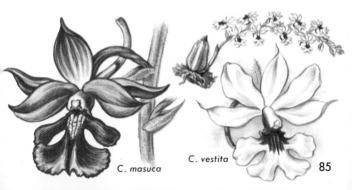

C. masuca

C. vestita

85

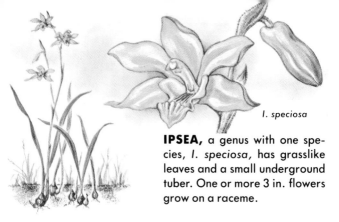

I. speciosa

IPSEA, a genus with one species, *I. speciosa,* has grasslike leaves and a small underground tuber. One or more 3 in. flowers grow on a raceme.

SPATHOGLOTTIS is a genus of terrestrial orchids (40 species) growing from northern India to the Pacific islands. The ovoid pseudobulbs bear a few plicate leaves. A succession of showy flowers is produced on the tall, slender raceme that arises from the base.

SPATHOGLOTTIS AUREA, of Malaya and Indonesia, has deep yellow flowers 2½ in. across. The lip lobes may have crimson spots. The 2 ft. plants are common in cool highlands.

SPATHOGLOTTIS PLICATA is a variable species with flowers ranging from bright purple to mauve or white. Flowers vary from less than 1 in. to 2 in. across. It is easily grown.

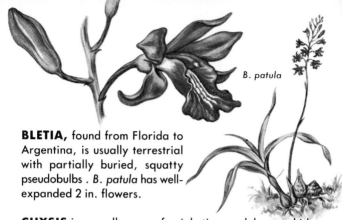

B. patula

BLETIA, found from Florida to Argentina, is usually terrestrial with partially buried, squatty pseudobulbs . *B. patula* has well-expanded 2 in. flowers.

CHYSIS is a small genus of epiphytic, pendulous orchids found throughout tropical America from Mexico to Peru and Venezuela. Its fleshy pseudobulbs, a foot or more long, are club-shaped. The plicate leaves sometimes drop before the long-lasting flowers appear.

CHYSIS AUREA produces up to 8 fragrant waxy flowers, 1½-2 in. across. The tawny yellow sepals, petals, and yellow throat are marked with blood-red.

CHYSIS BRACTESCENS has 10-12 fragrant 3 in. flowers with waxy white sepals and petals. The bracts are much longer than in C. *aurea.*

bract

bract

BULBOPHYLLUM is one of the largest genera of orchids—over 1,000 epiphytic species. The flowers are often so small (even minute) and ill-smelling that they are of little interest to orchid collectors. Flower sepals are larger than the petals and of various colors. The creeping rhizome bears nearly spherical or conical pseudobulbs usually topped with one or two leaves.

BULBOPHYLLUM BUFO has prominent 3 in. pseudobulbs bearing two 6 in. leaves. Small brown-purple flowers are borne on flattened, erect, spiraled flower stems. From Sierra Leone.

BULBOPHYLLUM MAKOY-ANUM, with ¾ in. avoid pseudobulbs, has purplish flower stalk with an umbel of 1½ in. flowers. It is sometimes put in the genus *Cirrhopetalum*.

BULBOPHYLLUM LOBBII has glossy, egg-shaped pseudobulbs up to 3 in. tall. Solitary flower may be 3 in. across; highly mobile lip. Native of Burma and Indonesia.

BULBOPHYLLUM MEDUSAE is a creeping plant with 1½ in. pseudobulbs. Inflorescence, 6 in. high, is a dense umbel of fragrant flowers with threadlike sepals up to 5 in. long.

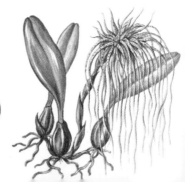

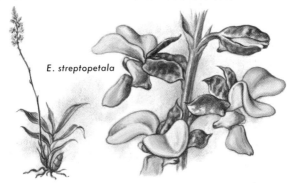

E. streptopetala

EULOPHIA is distributed throughout the tropics and sub-tropics with most of the 200 species in Africa. These terrestrials are variable in appearance, some with definite pseudobulbs and folded leaves. All have erect inflorescences of few to many flowers with a spurred lip. _E. streptopetala_, from South Africa, has a 2 in. conical pseudobulb and a 4-6 ft. raceme bearing many 1½ in. flowers. _E. alta_ occurs in all Americas and in Africa.

EULOPHIELLA, with just two species, is found only in Madagascar. Pseudobulbs are elongated, and foliage is plicate. Long-lasting beautiful flowers are produced on an erect or arching raceme. _E. elisabethae_ has up to 40 waxy flowers, 1½ in. across.

E. elisabethae

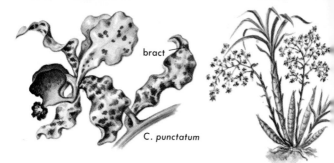

bract

C. punctatum

CYRTOPODIUM includes 12 epiphytic or terrestrial species found in Western Hemisphere tropics and subtropics. They have large clublike pseudobulbs with numerous deciduous leaves. The long panicle arises from the base and carries many flowers and colored bracts. C. *punctatum*, with spotted 2 in. flowers, is common from south Florida and Mexico to Brazil and Paraguay.

CYMBIDIELLA, with only a few species, is no longer considered a part of the genus *Cymbidium*. Pseudobulbs are prominent, at intervals on a rhizome. C. *pardalina* (= *rhodochila*) is a beautiful species from Madagascar with striking 3-4 in. flowers on 2-2½ ft. racemes.

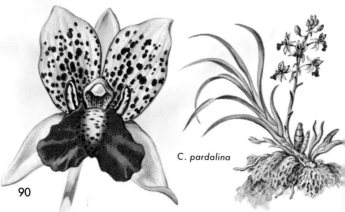

C. pardalina

CYMBIDIUM, a genus of terrestrial or epiphytic orchids from India to Australia, has about 50 species and several thousand horticultural hybrids. Pseudobulbs are usually short and the ribbonlike leaves are leathery. Racemes, erect or pendent, have many small to very large flowers. Many of the large-flowered hybrids are grown in out-of-doors beds in California.

CYMBIDIUM EBURNEUM has thin tubular pseudobulbs and long glossy leaves. The erect raceme carries two or more 3 in., waxy white flowers. From the Himalayas to Burma.

CYMBIDIUM PUMILUM, a dwarf species—6 to 12 in. high—from China and Japan, is used to make hybrid miniature cymbidiums. It has small (1 in.) red-brown flowers.

C. pumilum

C. eburneum

CYMBIDIUM DEVONIANUM is a compact species with small pseudobulbs and relatively broad leaves. The pendent raceme bears many closely set 1-1½ in., long-lived flowers. From India, Nepal, and Thailand.

CYMBIDIUM GIGANTEUM, with prominent, compressed pseudobulbs and 30 in. leaves, bears an arching raceme of 7-12 flowers, 4 in. across.

CYMBIDIUM FINLAYSON-IANUM has long, thick, leathery leaves without noticeable pseudobulbs. The raceme is pendulous, with numerous 1½-2 in., brownish-yellow, red-tinged flowers.

CYMBIDIUM HOOKERIA-NUM bears arching racemes of 6-12 green flowers, 4-5 in. across, with purple-spotted lips. Once called C. *grandiflorum.*

GRAMMATOPHYLLUM SPECIOSUM is truly the giant of the orchid world. The canelike pseudobulbs may reach 25 ft. in height but are usually shorter. Leaves are up to 2½ ft. long. The 5-8 ft. tall raceme may bear more than 100 flowers, each 5-6 in. across.

GRAMMATOPHYLLUM includes some of the largest orchid plants. Native to Asia and the Pacific, the dozen or so species have either elongated, canelike pseudobulbs or short clustered ones. Leaves are long and strap-shaped. The fleshy flowers are not brightly colored but are curiously marked with brown, red, or purple.

GRAMMATOPHYLLUM SCRIPTUM has short ridged stems with up to 100 flowers on an arching raceme. The fragrant 2 in. flowers are typically yellow-green with brown blotches.

GRAMMATOPHYLLUM PANTHERINUM has a growth habit similar to G. *speciosum*. Flowers are smaller with broader parts. From New Guinea and Pacific islands.

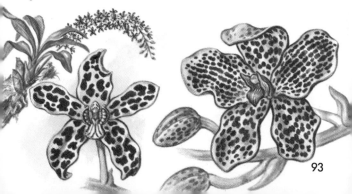

93

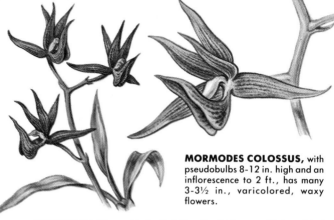

MORMODES COLOSSUS, with pseudobulbs 8-12 in. high and an inflorescence to 2 ft., has many 3-3½ in., varicolored, waxy flowers.

MORMODES, called Goblin Orchids or Flying-Bird Orchids, includes about 20 species of American tropical epiphytes. They have short, stocky pseudobulbs with deciduous, plicate leaves. The raceme, arising from the base or side of the pseudobulb, bears flowers that are variable in color, with lip and column twisting in opposite directions.

MORMODES IGNEUM produces one to several inflorescences per bulb. Each raceme has many flowers, variable in size and color, generally fragrant, reddish brown, and long lasting.

MORMODES BUCCINATOR, with pseudobulbs 4-8 in. tall, has foot-long racemes. The variable flowers range in color from white to deep yellow or brownish purple; about 2 in. across.

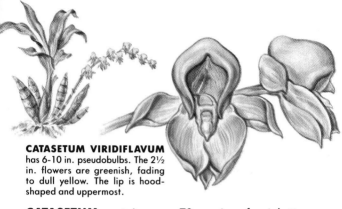

CATASETUM VIRIDIFLAVUM has 6-10 in. pseudobulbs. The 2½ in. flowers are greenish, fading to dull yellow. The lip is hood-shaped and uppermost.

CATASETUM contains over 70 species of epiphytic or occasionally semiterrestrial orchids. These orchids, found in the American tropics, have thick, stocky pseudobulbs. The large showy flowers are usually either male or female; sometimes bisexual. Male flowers in some species shoot the pollen masses with great force when the sensitive antennae are touched.

CATASETUM FIMBRIATUM produces 12-15 flowers, each about 2½ in. across. The green sepals and petals are spotted with red-brown and the white saclike lip is deeply fringed.

CATASETUM PILEATUM, also called C. *bungerothii,* has cylindric pseudobulbs to 8 in. tall. The arched raceme bears 6-10 fragrant, 3 in. blooms. From Venezuela, Trinidad, and Brazil.

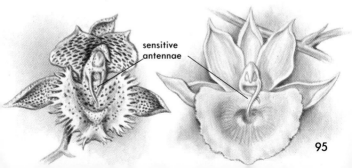

sensitive antennae

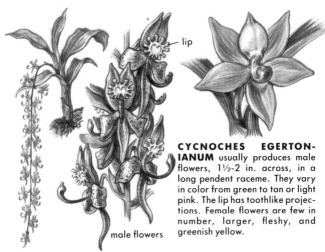

CYCNOCHES EGERTON-IANUM usually produces male flowers, 1½-2 in. across, in a long pendent raceme. They vary in color from green to tan or light pink. The lip has toothlike projections. Female flowers are few in number, larger, fleshy, and greenish yellow.

male flowers

CYCNOCHES, known as the Swan Orchid, contains about 12 species. The elongate pseudobulbs are cylindrical and fleshy, and the large plicate leaves soon fall. Flowers are few and large in some species, numerous and small in others; may be male, female, or rarely bisexual. Flowers of each sex are usually produced at different times on the same plant. Their long, curving column resembles the neck of a swan. The lip is uppermost.

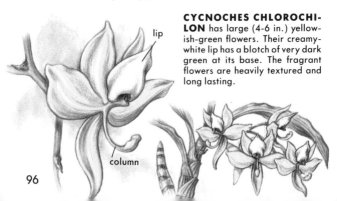

CYCNOCHES CHLOROCHILON has large (4-6 in.) yellowish-green flowers. Their creamy-white lip has a blotch of very dark green at its base. The fragrant flowers are heavily textured and long lasting.

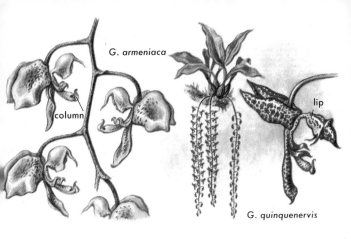

G. armeniaca

column

lip

G. quinquenervis

GONGORA (20 species of epiphytes) has heavily fragrant flowers that arch or hang down. They are sometimes called Punch-and-Judy Orchids. The pseudobulbs are wrinkled and have plicate leaves. The multicolored flowers are complicated in structure. G. armeniaca bears up to 30 waxy, 2 in. flowers, and G. quinquenervis has darker, 2 in. flowers.

STANHOPEA, a tropical American genus of over 50 species, has pendent inflorescences which arise from the base of single-leaved pseudobulbs. The flowers are large, short-lived, and fragrant. S. wardii is found from Mexico to Venezuela and Peru.

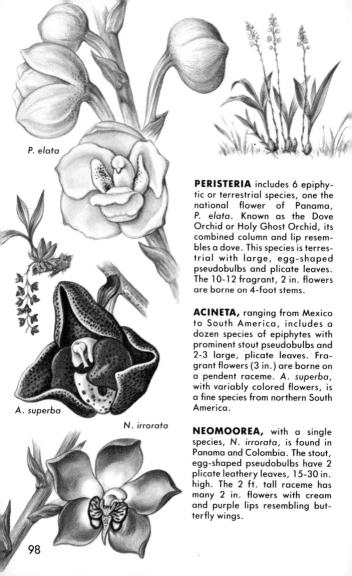

P. elata

A. superba

N. irrorata

PERISTERIA includes 6 epiphytic or terrestrial species, one the national flower of Panama, *P. elata*. Known as the Dove Orchid or Holy Ghost Orchid, its combined column and lip resembles a dove. This species is terrestrial with large, egg-shaped pseudobulbs and plicate leaves. The 10-12 fragrant, 2 in. flowers are borne on 4-foot stems.

ACINETA, ranging from Mexico to South America, includes a dozen species of epiphytes with prominent stout pseudobulbs and 2-3 large, plicate leaves. Fragrant flowers (3 in.) are borne on a pendent raceme. *A. superba*, with variably colored flowers, is a fine species from northern South America.

NEOMOOREA, with a single species, *N. irrorata*, is found in Panama and Colombia. The stout, egg-shaped pseudobulbs have 2 plicate leathery leaves, 15-30 in. high. The 2 ft. tall raceme has many 2 in. flowers with cream and purple lips resembling butterfly wings.

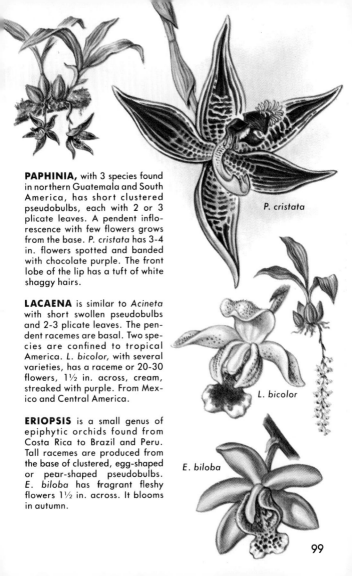

PAPHINIA, with 3 species found in northern Guatemala and South America, has short clustered pseudobulbs, each with 2 or 3 plicate leaves. A pendent inflorescence with few flowers grows from the base. *P. cristata* has 3-4 in. flowers spotted and banded with chocolate purple. The front lobe of the lip has a tuft of white shaggy hairs.

P. cristata

LACAENA is similar to *Acineta* with short swollen pseudobulbs and 2-3 plicate leaves. The pendent racemes are basal. Two species are confined to tropical America. *L. bicolor,* with several varieties, has a raceme or 20-30 flowers, 1½ in. across, cream, streaked with purple. From Mexico and Central America.

L. bicolor

ERIOPSIS is a small genus of epiphytic orchids found from Costa Rica to Brazil and Peru. Tall racemes are produced from the base of clustered, egg-shaped or pear-shaped pseudobulbs. *E. biloba* has fragrant fleshy flowers 1½ in. across. It blooms in autumn.

E. biloba

99

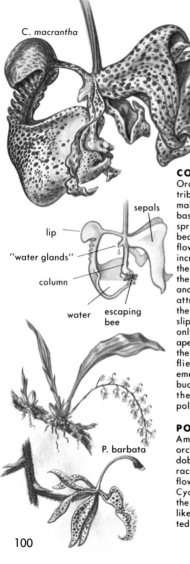

C. macrantha

sepals

lip

"water glands"

column

water   escaping
bee

P. barbata

CORYANTHES, the Bucket Orchid, comprises 15 species distributed from Belize and Guatemala to Brazil and Peru. From the base of tall tapered pseudobulbs springs a slender pendent raceme bearing 1 to 3 extremely complex flowers, pollination of which is an incredible story. Water glands fill the bucketlike lip with liquid up to the opening between the column and apex of the lip. The bees are attracted by the fleshy margins of the lip, not by the liquid. A bee slips and falls into the liquid. His only escape is by way of the lip apex where, as he crawls through, the pollinia stick to him. He then flies to another flower. On emerging from the liquid in this bucket, the bee leaves pollinia on the stigma, thus effecting pollination.

POLYCYCNIS is a tropical American genus of epiphytic orchids with short stemlike pseudobulbs and plicate leaves. The raceme, bearing twelve or more flowers with column arching as in Cycnoches, rises from the base of the stem. P. barbata has swanlike, orange-yellow, purple-dotted, 1½ in. flowers.

XYLOBIUM includes about 30 species of tropical American orchids with short or elongated pseudobulbs. The erect raceme with few to many flowers arises from the base of pseudobulbs. *X. elongatum* has heavily veined leaves and 5–15, pale-yellow flowers 1½ in. across.

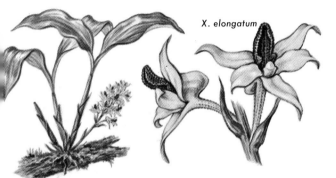

X. elongatum

BIFRENARIA, with 30 species from Panama to Brazil, has angular pseudobulbs and waxy leaves. The flowers, small to large, are produced from the base of pseudobulbs. *B. harrisoniae* has a solitary, leathery, shiny leaf and waxy 3 in. flowers, produced singly or in pairs. The lip is hairy and the color variable.

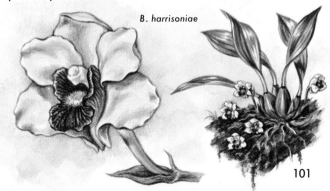

B. harrisoniae

LYCASTE has large, showy, long-lasting flowers with sepals much larger than the petals. The stout, ovoid pseudo-bulbs bear 1–3 large, plicate, deciduous leaves. In some species, after leaves have dropped sharp processes remain on top of the pseudobulbs. As each new pseudobulb forms, a number of erect stalks surround the base, each capped with a single flower.

LYCASTE SKINNERI is the national flower of Guatemala. Pseudobulbs, often angular, reach 8 in. tall, and the waxy, fragrant flowers may be 6 in. across. This species is routinely used in *Lycaste* hybridizing.

LYCASTE DEPPEI has large 4 in. flowers with pure white petals and pale-green sepals flecked with red. The lip has a bright-yellow pointed mid-lobe and yellow side lobes, marked with red. It is common in Mexico.

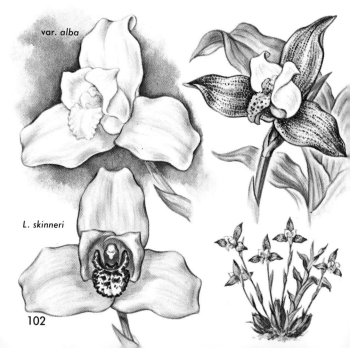

var. *alba*

L. skinneri

LYCASTE AROMATICA has 2 to 4 in. pseudobulbs and plicate, 8-20 in. leaves. Flower stalks, 4 in. tall, have 2½ in. waxy, fragrant flowers. Sepals are yellow, petals deeper yellow.

LYCASTE LONGIPETALA, also known as *L. gigantea*, has 3-5 in. pseudobulbs bearing two 3 ft. leaves. The large flowers (4-6 in.) are borne singly on 1 ft. erect peduncles. Native to Venezuela, Colombia, Peru and Ecuador.

LYCASTE CRUENTA has compressed pseudobulbs 4 in. tall and several leaves. Its flowers are 2½-4 in. across, with yellow-green sepals and bright-yellow to orange petals and lip.

LYCASTE SCHILLERIANA, another large-flowered species, has similar pseudobulbs but the leaves are shorter. The 4-5 in. flowers are dull in color, hence the species is not widely grown. From Peru and Colombia.

103

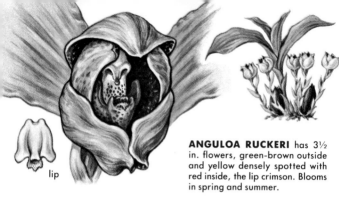

ANGULOA RUCKERI has 3½ in. flowers, green-brown outside and yellow densely spotted with red inside, the lip crimson. Blooms in spring and summer.

ANGULOA, with about 10 species in the Andean region of South America, is sometimes called the Tulip Orchid because of the shape of the flower or Cradle Orchid because the hinged fleshy lip rocks. All species have stout, more or less egg-shaped pseudobulbs, and broad, plicate leaves.

ANGULOA CLOWESII bears 2 ft. deciduous leaves and numerous 1 ft. stalks, each with a single, waxy, 3-4 in., citron or golden-yellow flower. Flowers have a cream to orange lip that is freely movable.

ANGULOA UNIFLORA has long, strongly plicate leaves with numerous single-flowered stalks. The fragrant flowers (3-4 in.) are cream white, spotted with pink. Several other color forms are known.

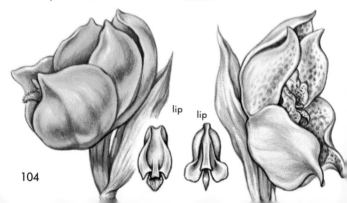

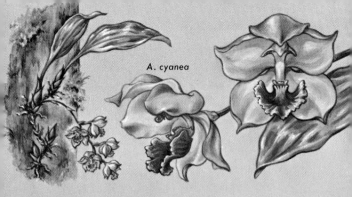

A. cyanea

SO-CALLED BLUE ORCHIDS are rare. Only a few genera have blue or near-blue flowers, and three of these are shown here. The most famous is *Acacallis*, from South America. *A. cyanea* (above) has racemes with 3–7 blue-violet flowers, 2–2½ in. in diameter.

PABSTIA, with a single species, *P. jugosa,* is a native of Brazil. The short, 2-leaved pseudobulbs bear erect racemes of 2 or 3 two-inch flowers with white sepals. Spots on petals and lip often have a blue-violet cast.

KOELLENSTEINIA is another genus with white to violet-blue flowers. *K. ionoptera,* with short clustered pseudobulbs and narrow pointed leaves, has 1 in. bright-violet flowers with white-tipped sepals and petals.

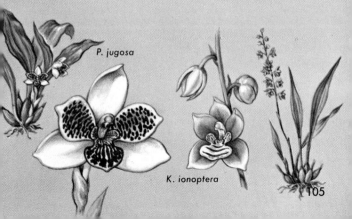

P. jugosa

K. ionoptera

105

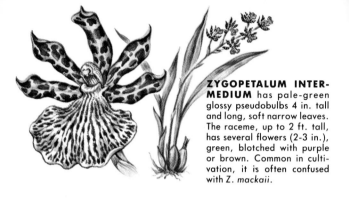

ZYGOPETALUM INTERMEDIUM has pale-green glossy pseudobulbs 4 in. tall and long, soft narrow leaves. The raceme, up to 2 ft. tall, has several flowers (2-3 in.), green, blotched with purple or brown. Common in cultivation, it is often confused with Z. *mackaii*.

ZYGOPETALUM is a genus of about 40 South American species but once included species now referred to other genera. From the base of medium-sized pseudobulbs arise inflorescences of brilliantly colored, long-lasting, fragrant flowers. The flat lip is always vividly marked.

ZYGOPETALUM MACKAII is similar to Z. *intermedium* but the petals are slightly shorter than the sepals, and the large, round lip is not hairy. Veining on lip is more distinctly lined.

ZYGOPETALUM CRINITUM is similar to the other two species, and may only be but a variety of Z. *mackaii*. The lip is hairer, the veining denser, and the flower stem stragglier.

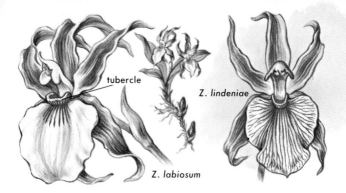

Z. lindeniae

Z. labiosum

tubercle

ZYGOSEPALUM has only a few species. Small flattened and grooved pseudobulbs bear 1 or more 10 in. leaves. At base of the lip is a fleshy U-shaped tubercle. *Z. labiosum* has attractive 4 in. flowers; the flowers of *Z. lindeniae* are slightly smaller. Native to Venezuela.

PROMENAEA includes 15 Brazilian species of dwarf epiphytes with short pseudobulbs, one or two leaves, and a drooping flower stalk. *P. xanthina* bears long-lasting, 2 in. citron-yellow flowers with a spotted lip. *P. stapelioides* has 1–2 flowers, also about 2 in., barred with deep purple, and a rich, almost black, 3–lobed lip.

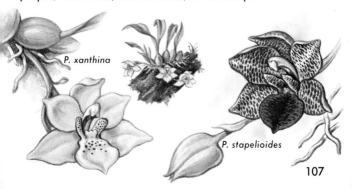

P. xanthina

P. stapelioides

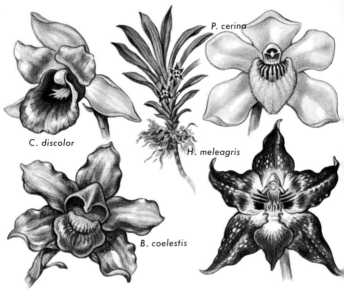

P. cerina

C. discolor

H. meleagris

B. coelestis

FAN-TYPE ORCHID PLANTS without pseudobulbs include several genera with attractive solitary flowers. Four such genera from the American tropics are shown.

COCHLEANTHES is a genus of 14 species whose fragrant flowers have a shell-like lip. The plant consists of a fan-shaped tuft of long leaves, without pseudobulbs. The rather fleshy, solitary flowers are produced on short stalks at the base of this fan. *C. discolor*, with 3 in. flowers, is commonly grown under the name *Chondrorhyncha discolor*.

BOLLEA is another genus of fan-shaped plants. *B. coelestis*, from Colombia, with solitary 3-4 in. flowers, is one of few "blue" orchids of the New World.

PESCATOREA includes 14 epiphytic species whose large solitary waxy flowers are borne on short stalks that emerge from the base of the leaf fan. *P. cerina*, with fragrant, fleshy, whitish flowers, 3-4 in. across, occurs in Costa Rica and Panama.

HUNTLEYA includes *H. meleagris* which has waxy, shiny flowers up to 4 in. across. Color varies from reddish brown to white and yellow. It is an attractive plant even when not in bloom. From Brazil, Venezuela, and Guyana.

MAXILLARIA (pp. 109-111) is a widely scattered genus of more than 300 epiphytic species which vary tremendously in appearance of the plant. Their sometimes inconspicuous pseudobulbs may be clustered on short rhizomes or scattered on long, sprawling or climbing rhizomes. Miniature species are less than 2 in. tall; others grow to several feet. Flowers may be very small (¼ in. or less) or large (6 in. or more across).

MAXILLARIA FUCATA, with clustered pseudobulbs, has thick-textured, brownish-red flowers 1½ in. across. It is a striking but rare species from Ecuador.

MAXILLARIA CAMARIDII has a long, sprawling rhizome with compressed, scattered pseudobulbs. The waxy, white, narcissus-scented flowers, over 2 in. across, last only one day.

MAXILLARIA PICTA is a Brazilian species with clustered pseudobulbs, strap-shaped leaves, and many solitary 1½ in. flowers that are white with spots outside and golden within.

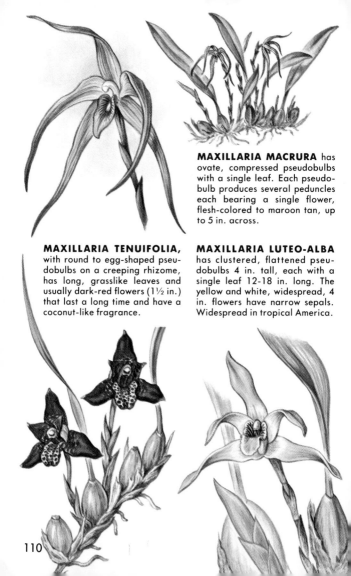

MAXILLARIA MACRURA has ovate, compressed pseudobulbs with a single leaf. Each pseudobulb produces several peduncles each bearing a single flower, flesh-colored to maroon tan, up to 5 in. across.

MAXILLARIA TENUIFOLIA, with round to egg-shaped pseudobulbs on a creeping rhizome, has long, grasslike leaves and usually dark-red flowers (1½ in.) that last a long time and have a coconut-like fragrance.

MAXILLARIA LUTEO-ALBA has clustered, flattened pseudobulbs 4 in. tall, each with a single leaf 12-18 in. long. The yellow and white, widespread, 4 in. flowers have narrow sepals. Widespread in tropical America.

M. valenzuelana

MAXILLARIA VALENZUE-LANA is a pendulous, epiphytic, fan-shaped plant. The 1 in. flowers are chiefly yellow and are produced at the base of the leaves, singly on short peduncles. They do not open fully.

M. sanderiana

MAXILLARIA SANDERIANA is considered to be the finest of all maxillarias. The large, 6 in. flowers with white sepals and petals, marked with blood-red, grow on semi-erect peduncles. The fleshy, waxy-white lip is stained with red and yellow. It is found at high elevations in the Andes of Ecuador and Peru.

MAXILLARIA SOPHRONI-TIS, a dwarf species from Venezuela, has 1 in. leaves on tiny pseudobulbs at intervals on a creeping rhizome. The scarlet-red flowers are less than 1 in. across.

M. sophronitis

111

S. steelei

Section of leaf

SCUTICARIA has short pseudobulbs and long, hanging, whiplike leaves, furrowed on one side. The 5 species are native to Brazil, Venezuela, and Guyana. S. steelei has leaves about 4 ft. long and 1-3 flowers in a hanging raceme. The flowers are waxy, long-lasting, and about 2-3 in. across.

TRIGONIDIUM, a genus of about 12 species, has solitary, urn-shaped flowers on long upright scapes. Pseudobulbs are 1-2 leaved. Petals are much smaller than the sepals. T. egertonianum, found from Mexico to Colombia, has clustered, egg-shaped pseudobulbs and long, narrow leaves. The 1½ in. flowers have a bluish, raised spot at tips of petals.

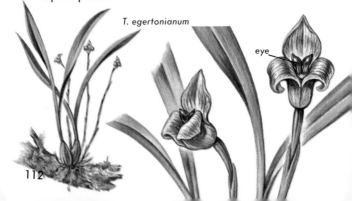

T. egertonianum

eye

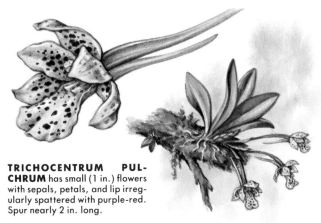

TRICHOCENTRUM PUL-CHRUM has small (1 in.) flowers with sepals, petals, and lip irregularly spattered with purple-red. Spur nearly 2 in. long.

TRICHOCENTRUM, a tropical American genus of a dozen species, has minute pseudobulbs and usually solitary, short leaves. One to 5 usually showy flowers open in succession. The lip extends into a short to long spur.

TRICHOCENTRUM ALBO-COCCINEUM has long-lived, wide-open flowers, 2 in. across. The tawny-brown and green sepals and petals contrast with the large white lip, marked with dark purple. Spur ½ in. long.

TRICHOCENTRUM TI-GRINUM has leaves specked with red. The 2 in. flowers are greenish yellow splotched with purplish brown. The white lip has three yellow keels on the crest. The spur is very short.

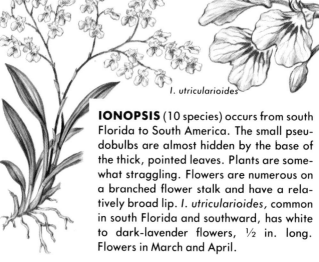

I. utricularioides

IONOPSIS (10 species) occurs from south Florida to South America. The small pseudobulbs are almost hidden by the base of the thick, pointed leaves. Plants are somewhat straggling. Flowers are numerous on a branched flower stalk and have a relatively broad lip. _I. utricularioides,_ common in south Florida and southward, has white to dark-lavender flowers, ½ in. long. Flowers in March and April.

COMPARETTIA, from Mexico to South America, has small pseudobulbs and relatively large, fleshy leaves. C. _coccinea_ and C. _falcata_ are similar but differ in color of the flowers. In C. _coccinea,_ the petals and sepals are orange, the lip scarlet and adorned with two yellow keels. In C. _falcata_ the 1¼ in. flowers are usually a magenta-rose, with one white keel on the lip.

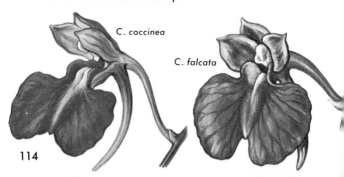

C. coccinea

C. falcata

RODRIGUEZIA, from Costa Rica to Brazil and Peru, includes about 35 dwarf species, all epiphytic plants. The small pseudobulbs usually have a single leaf. One or more arching racemes carry several to many attractive flowers. A wide range of colors is found in this group of dainty but showy orchids.

RODRIGUEZIA SECUNDA, with compressed, clustered pseudobulbs and leathery dark-green leaves, produces 1-6 racemes per growth. The flowers (½ in. across), from white to rose-red, grow on one side of the inflorescence.

RODRIGUEZIA BRACTEATA has a drooping raceme with numerous fragrant white flowers, 1½ in. long, with golden keels on the lip. It comes from Brazil.

RODRIGUEZIA BATEMANII has only a few flowers on a hanging raceme. Each flower is 2 in. long, generally white with rose-purple markings but color varies.

▼ ▼

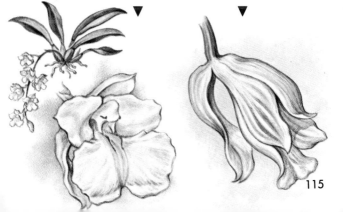

TRICHOPILIA has large, *Cattleya*-like flowers, often with twisted sepals and petals and a more or less funnel-shaped lip. The flattened, clustered pseudobulbs each bear a single leathery leaf.

TRICHOPILIA TORTILIS, from Central America, produces a slender pendent raceme with fragrant 5 in. flowers, each with narrow, strongly twisted petals and sepals.

TRICHOPILIA SUAVIS, with broad, compressed, crowded pseudobulbs, has an arching raceme of 2-5 fragrant, 4 in. flowers, variable in color. The lip is crisped or frilled.

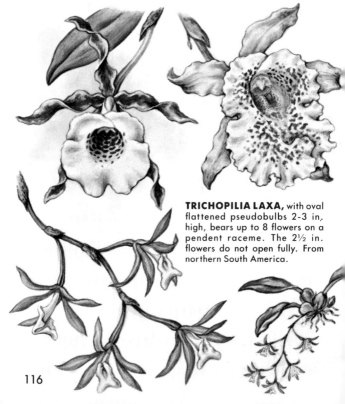

TRICHOPILIA LAXA, with oval flattened pseudobulbs 2-3 in. high, bears up to 8 flowers on a pendent raceme. The 2½ in. flowers do not open fully. From northern South America.

C. *noezliana*

COCHLIODA is a genus of high-altitude orchids from Ecuador, Peru, and Bolivia. All 6 species have short pseudobulbs and brilliantly colored flowers. C. *noezliana* with its many vivid scarlet flowers (1¼ in.) has been hybridized with *Oncidium*, *Miltonia*, and *Odontoglossum*.

GOMESA, with about 20 dwarf species, found in Brazil, has compressed pseudobulbs with 1 or 2 leaves. The arched racemes carry numerous, small, sweet-scented flowers. Those of G. *crispa* are ¾ in. long and yellow-green.

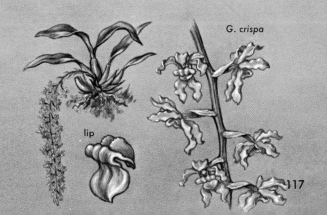

G. *crispa*

lip

117

ODONTOGLOSSUM, with over 100 known species from Mexico and South America, is predominantly a genus of orchids from high elevations, hence cool-growing, but some species come from warm lowlands. Pseudobulbs are prominent, with 1-3 leaves at the top. An inflorescence may bear from one to many showy and often large flowers. Hundreds of hybrids have been made within the genus. Such genera as *Oncidium, Miltonia, Cochlioda, Brassia,* and others have been crossed with *Odontoglossum* to yield multigeneric hybrids.

ODONTOGLOSSUM COR-ONARIUM (also known as *Otoglossum brevifolium*) produces erect inflorescences with many 2 in., glossy, red-copper flowers bordered with yellow.

ODONTOGLOSSUM BLAN-DUM is a dwarf plant with slender leaves about 9 in. long. The raceme is semi-erect with small (1½ in.) white flowers, spotted with red-purple.

ODONTOGLOSSUM CRIS-PUM is one of the most variable and handsome species of *Odontoglossum.* Atop the egg-shaped pseudobulbs are 2 or 3 soft-textured leaves. The inflorescence has many variable 3 in. flowers, mostly white or pale rose, often spotted. Numerous and named varieties have been described.

some color variations

ODONTOGLOSSUM CIR-RHOSUM has flat pseudobulbs and a dozen or more 4 in. flowers with narrow, tapering petals and sepals, white spotted with red-brown. Found in the Andes.

ODONTOGLOSSUM MACU-LATUM has 3 in. flowers on an arching inflorescence. Sepals are chestnut-brown or purplish; petals are yellow spotted with brown.

ODONTOGLOSSUM ROSSII has 2 to 5 three-inch flowers on a spike. Their color is variable, but they are usually white or pink spotted with dark brown. This species comes from Mexico.

ROSSIOGLOSSUM GRANDE, the Tiger Orchid, has clustered, 4 in. pseudobulbs. Up to 9 or more flowers, 4 to 6 in. across, are borne on an upright raceme.

ODONTOGLOSSUM LUTEO-PURPUREUM is a variable species with 3-4 in. flowers with chestnut-brown sepals and petals marked with yellow. The fringed yellow lip has a chestnut blotch.

ODONTOGLOSSUM TRIUM-PHANS is a variable Colombian species with 3 in. yellow flowers, marked with red-brown. There is a purple blotch on the white lip.

ODONTOGLOSSUM URO-SKINNERI, a Guatemalan species, has 10 to 30 showy flowers (2-3 in.) with greenish sepals and petals mottled with brown. The lip is usually rose-colored.

ODONTOGLOSSUM CER-VANTESII is a dwarf Mexican species with 4 to 6 rounded, 2 in. flowers streaked with concentric reddish-brown lines.

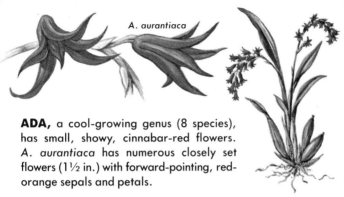
A. aurantiaca

ADA, a cool-growing genus (8 species), has small, showy, cinnabar-red flowers. *A. aurantiaca* has numerous closely set flowers (1½ in.) with forward-pointing, red-orange sepals and petals.

ASPASIA (about 6 species) is found from Central to South America. The plants are epiphytic, with short, erect pseudobulbs and a lateral raceme. Flower has lip at right angle to the column.

ASPASIA PRINCIPISSA has stalked, compressed pseudobulbs with a pair of leathery leaves. On the raceme are a few 2 in. flowers. Each has a large, wavy, creamy-white lip that becomes yellow with age.

ASPASIA VARIEGATA has clustered, compressed, 2-edged pseudobulbs with a pair of elongated thin leaves. The single 2 in. flower is yellow-green penciled with brown; the 3-lobed lip is streaked with purple.

BRASSIA includes about 20 species known as Spider Orchids that are found from south Florida and the West Indies to Mexico, Brazil, and Peru. Pseudobulbs have 1 to 3 leaves and lateral flower spikes. Sepals are commonly long and slender and vary in length.

BRASSIA CAUDATA, native from Florida and the West Indies to Panama, has showy flowers (2½ in. across) with orange-yellow sepals and petals, spotted with reddish brown. The lip is greenish yellow, blotched at the base. Sepals are 3-8 in. long.

BRASSIA GIREOUDIANA, with flattened pseudobulbs, has two glossy leaves more than 1 ft. long. The long-lasting, fragrant flowers are 8-10 in. long. Their color is yellow or greenish yellow blotched with dark brown at base of the flower segments.

BRASSIA ARCUIGERA, with orange-yellow flowers, has petals 2-3 in. long and an upper sepal somewhat longer. The tapered lateral sepals are 7 to 8 in. long or even longer.

BRASSIA VERRUCOSA has very dark pseudobulbs with 2 leaves. The showy, 4 to 6 in. flowers are fragrant and long lasting. The lip is conspicuously warty. Up to 40 flowers occur on a raceme.

BRASSIA MACULATA has showy, greenish-yellow flowers with purple markings. The lip is cream-white, spotted with purple. First found in Jamaica.

ADA ALLENII (formerly in the genus *Brassia*) lacks pseudobulbs. The racemes are shorter than the leaves. Flowers are 2½ in. across and sweetly scented.

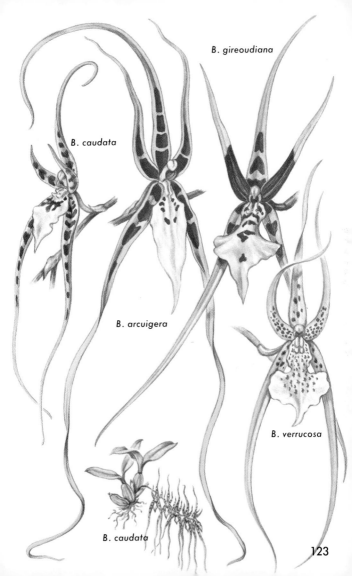

B. gireoudiana

B. caudata

B. arcuigera

B. verrucosa

B. caudata

123

var. *bicolor*

var. *moreliana*

MILTONIA SPECTABILIS has single, almost flat flowers to 3 in. or more across, and variable in color. Some have white sepals and petals with a purple lip. The var. *moreliana* has plum-purple sepals and petals and a bright rose-purple lip.

MILTONIA, with about 20 species, once contained a few high-elevation species now removed to the genus *Miltoniopsis*. The raceme, produced from the base of the pseudobulb, has 1 to 10 showy, long-lasting flowers. Numerous hybrids have been made among species of these genera and with *Oncidium*, *Odontoglossum*, *Brassia*, and other related genera.

M. *spectabilis*

MILTONIOPSIS VEXILLARIA has several flattened flowers up to 3½ in. long, variable in color from pure white to deep rose, sometimes blotched. The 2½ in. lip has a prominent yellow crest. It is native to Colombia and northern Ecuador.

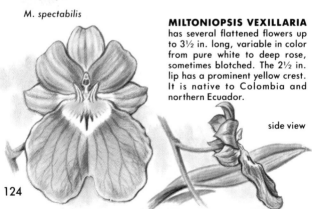

side view

124

MILTONIOPSIS ROEZLII, from Colombia, bears 1 to 4 flat, white flowers with a purple blotch at the base of each petal. The showy flowers (3-3½ in.) appear twice a year.

MILTONIA FLAVESCENS produces a raceme of up to ten 3 in. star-shaped flowers, with narrow straw-yellow sepals and petals and a white lip marked with red-purple. It comes from Brazil.

MILTONIA CANDIDA, another fine Brazilian species, produces racemes, each with 6 to 10, yellow to red-brown flowers, about 2½ in. across. The foliage is normally yellowish.

MILTONIOPSIS PHALAEN-OPSIS, a Colombian species, has pale-green grasslike leaves with a short raceme of one to three flat 1-2 in. white flowers. The lip is streaked with crimson.

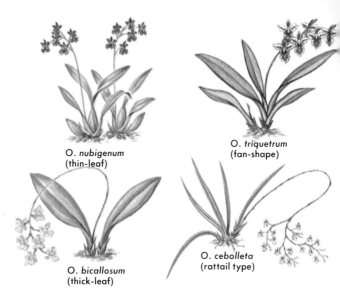

O. nubigenum
(thin-leaf)

O. triquetrum
(fan-shape)

O. bicallosum
(thick-leaf)

O. cebolleta
(rattail type)

ONCIDIUM is a genus of over 400 species; most are found in South America, some in Central America and the Caribbean area, and a few in Florida. Oncidiums are primarily epiphytic. Flowers are commonly yellow, but pink, white, and brown forms occur. Flower size varies from less than ¼ in. to over 4 in. Many of the species are called Dancing Ladies because the long inflorescences resemble groups of ballet dancers. Examples of some different types of growth are illustrated on this page. O. nubigenum (the thin-leaved type, others on pp. 128-130) is from Colombia, Ecuador, and Peru. O. triquetrum (other fan-shaped types, p. 127) is from Jamaica; O. bicallosum (the thick-leaved type, p. 131) is from Mexico, El Salvador, and Guatemala; and O. cebolleta (rattail type, p. 132) from Mexico to Paraguay.

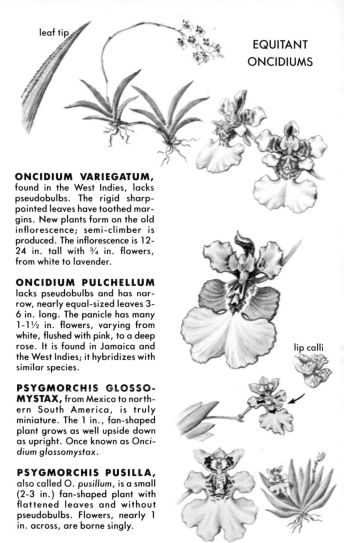

leaf tip

ONCIDIUM VARIEGATUM, found in the West Indies, lacks pseudobulbs. The rigid sharp-pointed leaves have toothed margins. New plants form on the old inflorescence; semi-climber is produced. The inflorescence is 12-24 in. tall with ¾ in. flowers, from white to lavender.

ONCIDIUM PULCHELLUM lacks pseudobulbs and has narrow, nearly equal-sized leaves 3-6 in. long. The panicle has many 1-1½ in. flowers, varying from white, flushed with pink, to a deep rose. It is found in Jamaica and the West Indies; it hybridizes with similar species.

lip calli

PSYGMORCHIS GLOSSO-MYSTAX, from Mexico to northern South America, is truly miniature. The 1 in., fan-shaped plant grows as well upside down as upright. Once known as *Oncidium glossomystax.*

PSYGMORCHIS PUSILLA, also called *O. pusillum,* is a small (2-3 in.) fan-shaped plant with flattened leaves and without pseudobulbs. Flowers, nearly 1 in. across, are borne singly.

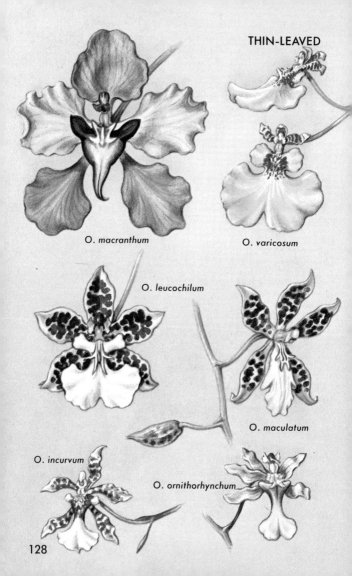

THIN-LEAVED

O. macranthum

O. varicosum

O. leucochilum

O. maculatum

O. incurvum

O. ornithorhynchum

128

ONCIDIUMS

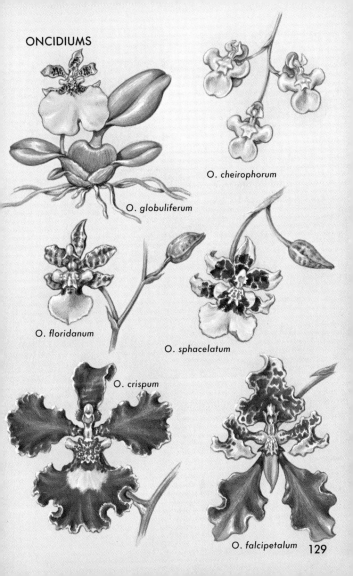

O. globuliferum

O. cheirophorum

O. floridanum

O. sphacelatum

O. crispum

O. falcipetalum

129

ONCIDIUM MACRANTHUM, with a very long, loosely branched inflorescence and nearly 4 in. flowers, has bright-yellow petals and yellow sepals shaded with olive-brown. The lip is white, bordered with violet-purple. Several varieties are cultivated.

ONCIDIUM VARICOSUM, with oval, furrowed pseudo-bulbs, produces 3-5 ft. stalks of 2 in., variable flowers, yellow and brown. In one variety the lip is 2-3 in. across.

ONCIDIUM LEUCOCHILUM, large plants with ovoid pseudo-bulbs, each with one to two leaves. The reddish-brown and white flowers are nearly 2 in. across. The white lip is deeply 3-lobed.

ONCIDIUM MACULATUM has 2 in. yellowish-green flowers blotched with brown. The lip is whitish marked with reddish-brown lines at the base.

ONCIDIUM INCURVUM has 3-4 in. ribbed pseudobulbs and a long panicle (3-7 ft.) with 1 in. rose and white flowers. It is a native of Mexico.

ONCIDIUM ORNITHO-RHYNCHUM has 1-2 in. pseudobulbs and 1-2 ft. panicles of many 1 in. rose-lilac flowers. It is sporadic from Mexico to Costa Rica.

ONCIDIUM GLOBULI-FERUM, with 1 in., round, flattened, single-leaved pseudobulbs, bears solitary 1 in. flowers on short scapes. Slender twisting rhizomes form tangled mats in the crowns of large trees in wet highland forests from Costa Rica to Peru.

ONCIDIUM CHEIROPHO-RUM is a dwarf plant with compressed egg-shaped pseudobulbs. The hanging panicle bears ½ in. flowers that are bright yellow and fragrant.

ONCIDIUM FLORIDANUM, found in Florida and the West Indies, is terrestrial or epiphytic with stout pseudobulbs and long leaves. The greenish-yellow 1 in. flowers are widely spaced on an upright panicle.

ONCIDIUM SPHACELATUM, with stout, clustered pseudobulbs and 15-24 in. leaves, produces 3-5 ft. spikes of 1 in., brown-and-yellow flowers.

ONCIDIUM CRISPUM, with brownish pseudobulbs and broad leaves, has large (3 in.), variable, chestnut-brown flowers. The crisped margins are yellow.

ONCIDIUM FALCIPETALUM has large pseudobulbs with one or two leaves. The panicle, up to 15 ft. long, bears many 3 in. flowers at the tip.

ONCIDIUM LURIDUM grows from Florida to South America. Commonly called the Mule Ear Orchid, its pseudobulbs are very small, and the rigid solitary leaf 5 to 35 in. long. The numerous, variable 1½-2 in. flowers are splotched with red-brown.

ONCIDIUM CARTHAGE-NENSE is similar to O. *luridum* but the leaves are often blotched with lavender, magenta, or red. From Florida to the West Indies and northern South America.

ONCIDIUM LINDENI resembles a small O. *luridum* in plant growth. Leaves are seldom over 4 in. long. The long flower stalk produces ½ in. flowers in succession. The dark-brown sepals and petals are offset by a fleshy, dark-red, shiny lip.

ONCIDIUM LANCEANUM, with deep-green leaves spotted with reddish purple, has very small pseudobulbs. The 2-3 in. fragrant flowers have a rose-purple lip.

131

OTHER POPULAR ONCIDIUMS

ONCIDIUM JONESIANUM, one of the rattail oncidiums, has pendulous, tapering, cylindric leaves. The arched raceme bears 10-15 long-lasting flowers, each 2-3 in. across. Native to south Brazil and Paraguay.

ONCIDIUM PAPILIO (known botanically as *Psychopsis papilia*) has round, flattened pseudobulbs and green leaves spotted with purple. The 6 in. high flowers are produced singly in succession at the flattened top of a long flower stalk. Commonly called the Butterfly Orchid.

ONCIDIUM AMPLIATUM has flattened turtle-shaped pseudobulbs spotted with purple. The 3 ft., arching inflorescence bears many 1½ in. clear yellow flowers with paddle-shaped petals. The mid-lobe of lip is very broad.

ONCIDIUM SPLENDIDUM has 2 in. compressed pseudobulbs, each with a leathery leaf 9-15 in. long. The erect panicle is 2-3 ft. tall with 3 in., long-lasting flowers. Because of the bars on the petals and sepals, it is called the Tiger Orchid.

L. oerstedii

flower enlarged

LOCKHARTIA, the Braided Orchid (about 30 epiphytic species), is named for the braided appearance of the leafy stems. Inflorescences grow from axils of the upper leaves and persist after the flowers drop. *L. oerstedii,* common from Mexico to Panama, has bright-yellow ¾ in. flowers; lip is spotted.

ORNITHOCEPHALUS is a genus of about 50 species. All lack pseudobulbs and have leaves arranged in a fan. The tiny, cupped, complex flowers have the anther in the shape of a bird's head, hence the name. *O. bicornis* forms a rigid 2-3½ in. grayish-green fan. The greenish-white ¼ in. flowers are fuzzy.

column and base of lip

O. bicornis

flower enlarged

133

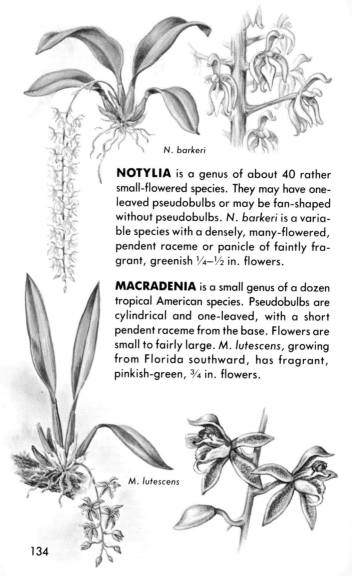

N. barkeri

NOTYLIA is a genus of about 40 rather small-flowered species. They may have one-leaved pseudobulbs or may be fan-shaped without pseudobulbs. *N. barkeri* is a variable species with a densely, many-flowered, pendent raceme or panicle of faintly fragrant, greenish ¼–½ in. flowers.

MACRADENIA is a small genus of a dozen tropical American species. Pseudobulbs are cylindrical and one-leaved, with a short pendent raceme from the base. Flowers are small to fairly large. *M. lutescens*, growing from Florida southward, has fragrant, pinkish-green, ¾ in. flowers.

M. lutescens

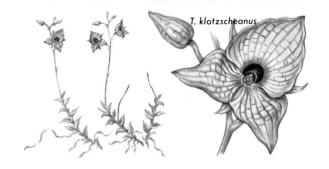

T. klotzscheanus

TELIPOGON (about 60 species) ranges from Costa Rica to Brazil and Bolivia. It has short narrow leaves and lacks pseudobulbs. Flowers are usually large for the plant. Sepals are almost hidden by petals and lip. *T. klotzscheanus* from Colombia and Venezuela has greenish 1-1½ in. flowers with strongly marked veins of green or purple.

DICHAEA is a tropical American orchid with perhaps as many as 35 species. Plants grow erect or pendent. They lack pseudobulbs, and the leaf bases overlap. Flowers grow singly on short stalks from axils of leaves. *D. panamensis* has stems 2-8 in. tall, and small ½ in. greenish-white flowers with red or purple spots.

D. panamensis

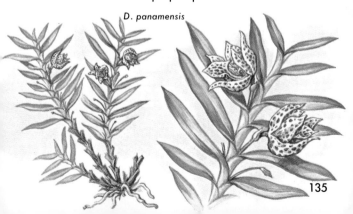

SARCOCHILUS has horizontal or climbing stems with fleshy leaves (sometimes absent) and many short-lived flowers on either drooping or upright spikes or racemes. The peduncles may be smooth or prickly and rough. The lip may be spurred or saclike.

CHILOSCHISTA LUNIFERA, from Burma, Thailand, and India, usually lacks leaves but has long straggly roots. The drooping flower stems bear many ½ in. flowers. Once known as *Sarcochilus luniferus.*

SARCOCHILUS HARTMANNII, from Australia, has a honeylike fragrance. It has upright leafy stems with spikes of 10 to 18 glistening white flowers (¾ in.). Lip and base of sepals and petals have reddish markings.

C. lunifera

S. hartmannii

RHYNCHOSTYLIS is an Asian genus of only 4 species, called the Foxtail Orchids because of their brushlike racemes of colorful flowers. The stems are short; the long, fleshy leaves are narrow with pale longitudinal lines. Flowers have a backward-pointing spur on the lip.

RHYNCHOSTYLIS GIGANTEA, from Burma, Indo-China, and Thailand, has short stems with foot-long, heavy leaves. The waxy, 1 in. flowers vary from pure white to deep red-violet.

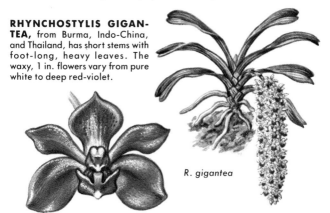

R. gigantea

RHYNCHOSTYLIS RETUSA is up to 2 ft. tall with tongue-shaped, 12-18 in. leaves. The fragrant, waxy flowers are ¾ in. across and variable in color. They form a densely packed, cylindrical, hanging raceme.

RHYNCHOSTYLIS VIOLACEA has leaves about 1 ft. long. The 1 in. flowers have a purple lip that is 3-lobed and has 5 fleshy ridges at the base. Sepals are white and petals sparingly but prominently streaked with purple.

▼   ▼

AERIDES MULTIFLORUM has a stout, sometimes long stem with narrow 10 in. leaves and numerous 1-2 in. white and purple flowers. The small spur of lip points forward under the mid-lobe.

AERIDES is a genus of epiphytes found from India to Japan and Malaysia. Over 20 species are known. All have fairly long stems, sometimes branching, with flat or rounded leaves and many medium, closely set flowers. Like *Rhynchostylis* (p. 137), they have also been called Foxtail Orchids. Many are delightfully scented.

AERIDES ODORATUM has stems which are often quite long, with fleshy, curved 10 in. leaves. The strongly scented flowers are white, spotted with purple, 1-2 in. long. The spur of the lip curves upward.

AERIDES ODORATUM var. LAWRENCEAE, with very long leaves, is sometimes considered a distinct species, *A. lawrenceae.* The flowers are 2 in. or more long; prominent 3-lobed lip, the middle lobe almost entirely purple.

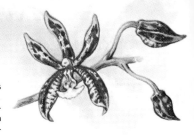

PHALAENOPSIS MANNII has green leaves spotted with violet. The 2 in. flowers are golden yellow, barred, and blotched with chestnut-brown. The lip is 3-lobed. A native of India.

PHALAENOPSIS, the Moth Orchid, is among the most beautiful of all orchids. About 46 species are known from India to the Philippines, New Guinea, and Australia. All have very short stems with a few, usually wide, leathery leaves. Inflorescences may have only one long-lasting flower but usually have more.

PHALAENOPSIS STUART-IANA has leaves mottled when young, gray-green with purple underneath when mature. The inflorescences have many 2 in. flowers. Lateral sepals are white to cream-colored, spotted with purple-red. (p. 140)

PHALAENOPSIS SCHILLER-IANA has dull-green leaves mottled with silver-gray, often purple underneath. The numerous 2½ in., pale-mauve flowers shade to white. From the Philippines. (p. 140)

PHALAENOPSIS LUEDDE-MANNIANA has waxy, yellowish-green leaves and a short, zig-zag stalk with 2-7 flowers. These are about 2 in. across; quite variable in color, this species is often confused with other lesser-known species. (p. 141)

PHALAENOPSIS VIOLACEA has shiny dark-green leaves and a short, flattened, zig-zag stalk with 2-2½ in. flowers produced one or two in succession. The flowers occur in two forms — Bornean and Malayan. (p. 140)

PHALAENOPSIS AMABILIS has a few dull-green, leathery leaves up to about 1 ft. long and 5 in. wide. The arching inflorescence has 6-20 flat, white flowers, up to 4 in. across. (p. 141)

PHALAENOPSIS CORNU-CERVI has bright glossy-green leaves, 6-10 in. long. The inflorescence is flattened at the top and produces 6-12 flowers in succession. The flowers are under 2 in. across. A native of Java, Sumatra, Borneo, Burma, Thailand, and parts of Malaysia. (p. 141)

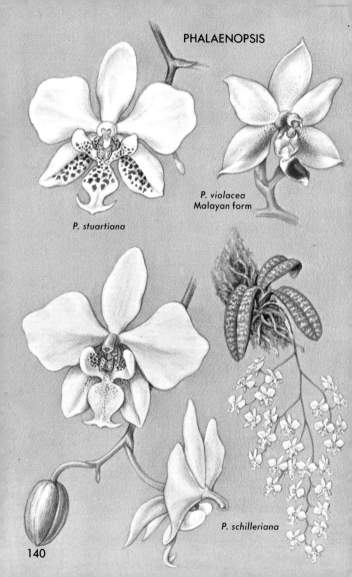

P. stuartiana

P. violacea
Malayan form

P. schilleriana

P. amabilis

P. lueddemanniana

P. cornu-cervi

141

VANDA, with about 40 species extending from India to New Guinea and northern Australia, varies in vegetative form and flower. Stems are usually stout, often long, mostly with short spaces between the strap-shaped or cylindrical leaves. Flowers are usually flat with a short spur on the lip. They are generally long-lasting. Hundreds of hybrids have been produced within the genus and with other genera.

VANDA SANDERIANA, the finest of the *Vanda* species, has been separated by some botanists into the genus *Euanthe*, due to a difference in lip structure. The flat, 3-5 in. flowers are of importance in hybridization, as this species can be crossed with species of many related genera. It comes from the Philippines.

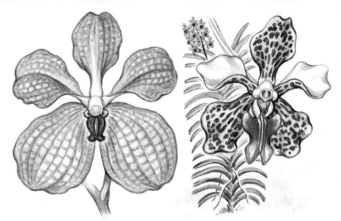

VANDA COERULEA with stems 1-3 ft. tall, produces variable 3-4 in. flowers with sepals and petals lighter than dark-blue lip. Petals are slightly twisted. Color varies from bluish white to deep blue or even pink.

VANDA DENISONIANA typically has 2½ in. waxy white flowers, but the variety *hebraica*, with sulfur-yellow flowers spotted with orange-yellow or brown, is most commonly grown.

VANDA TRICOLOR, from Java and Laos, may grow to several feet tall with 7-12 fragrant, waxy flowers, 2-3 in. across; white to yellow; densely spotted with red-brown. Petals usually have a 180° twist.

VANDA LUZONICA has 2-2½ in. flowers with a few crimson spots and a bright-purple lip. In form it may strongly resemble *V. tricolor* (above). From the Philippines.

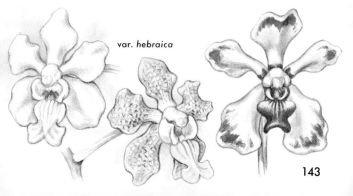

var. *hebraica*

143

VANDA PUMILA grows only 6-18 in. high; leaves 4-5 in. long. The raceme bears 2-3 flowers, about 2 in. across; the sepals are incurved, the petals twisted. The creamy-white color is often dotted with red. From India, Bhutan, and Thailand.

VANDA SPATHULATA has tall, climbing stems with purple-flushed leaves. The 1-1½ in., clear-yellow, flattish flowers are borne in succession, with up to three open at once. Native of Sri Lanka and S. India.

VANDA TERES has slender, round, branching stems, often climbing, with cylindrical leaves 4-8 in. long. Flowers, 3-4 in. across, on the upper part of the stem. Spur is funnel-shaped.

ARACHNIS, with about 10 species found from the Himalayas to New Guinea, is usually tall or vinelike, though some species are short-stemmed. The shape and color of the flowers give them the name of Scorpion Orchids; the curved lateral sepals represent the claws and the dorsal sepal the tail of the scorpion.

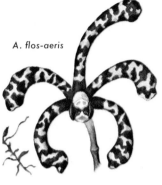

A. flos-aeris

ARACHNIS FLOS-AERIS is a climbing plant more than 15 ft. tall. The inflorescence may be 4 ft. long with 3½-4½ in. flowers. Common in Malaysia, Borneo, and Philippines, it has a musky odor.

ARACHNIS MAINGAYI is similar to A. flos-aeris but the stems are red-brown when old. Flowers are 3 in. across. It may be a natural hybrid between A. hookeriana and A. flos-aeris.

ESMERALDA CATHCARTII, often pendulous, grows 2-4 ft. long. The flowers are 3 in. or more in diameter. It is a native of the Himalayas. Once known as Arachnis cathcartii.

145

RENANTHERA, a genus found throughout tropical Asia and on many Pacific Islands, includes tall and climbing plants with panicles of red or red-and-yellow flowers. They have been used in hybridization to introduce their red color into vandas (p. 142).

RENANTHERA IMSCHOO-TIANA is less than 3 ft. tall, with rigid leaves. The panicle, up to 1½ ft. long, bears many 2¼ in. flowers— scarlet or yellow spotted with scarlet.

RENANTHERA STORIEI grows to 10-15 ft. tall with leaves to 10 in. long. The numerous dark-orange and crimson flowers are about 2½-3 in. long.

RENANTHERA MONACHICA is a Philippine species with 1½ in. flowers, yellow or orange with red spots. Its fleshy bluish-green leaves are from 3-5 in. long.

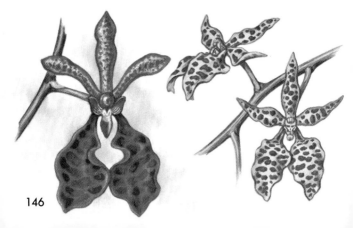

ASCOCENTRUM includes less than 10 species of small plants, all with the growth habit of vandas. The small flowers are often brilliantly colored. *Ascocentrum* ranges from the Himalayas to Taiwan and the Philippines. It has been crossed with *Vanda* to make compact hybrids.

ASCOCENTRUM MINIATUM is a dwarf orchid, less than 6 in. tall, with narrow, rigid leaves. Flowers (½ in.), from yellow-orange to orange-red, densely crowd the 4-6 in. raceme.

ASCOCENTRUM AMPULLA-CEUM has a stem 3-8 in. tall with 5-6 in. long leaves. The erect raceme has numerous 1 in., rose-carmine flowers.

ASCOCENTRUM MICRAN-THUM (now placed in the genus *Smitinandia*) has many small, white flowers often spotted with purple.

▼

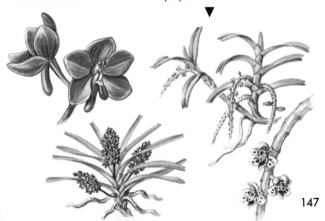

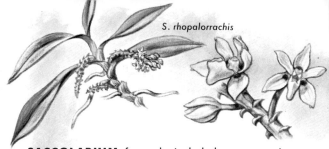

S. rhopalorrachis

SACCOLABIUM formerly included many species now placed in other genera. Now only a few species are left. The flowers are rather small with an immovable lip. *S. rhopalorrachis*, from Java and Malaya, has fragrant, ¼ in. flowers, produced in succession but each lasting only one day.

GASTROCHILUS, with about 20 species from India to Malaysia, has a short to long stem with a few leaves close together. Often two short inflorescences occur at a node, each with up to 10 flowers.

GASTROCHILUS CALCEO-LARIS has 2 in. inflorescences bearing a few ½ in. flowers that are greenish or yellowish with red-brown spots.

GASTROCHILUS DASYPO-GON has bright yellow sepals and petals, spotted with brownish purple. The saclike lip is white. The flowers are ¾-1 in. across.

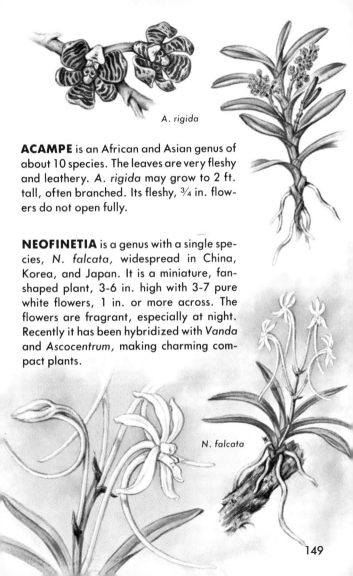

A. rigida

ACAMPE is an African and Asian genus of about 10 species. The leaves are very fleshy and leathery. *A. rigida* may grow to 2 ft. tall, often branched. Its fleshy, ¾ in. flowers do not open fully.

NEOFINETIA is a genus with a single species, *N. falcata*, widespread in China, Korea, and Japan. It is a miniature, fan-shaped plant, 3-6 in. high with 3-7 pure white flowers, 1 in. or more across. The flowers are fragrant, especially at night. Recently it has been hybridized with *Vanda* and *Ascocentrum*, making charming compact plants.

N. falcata

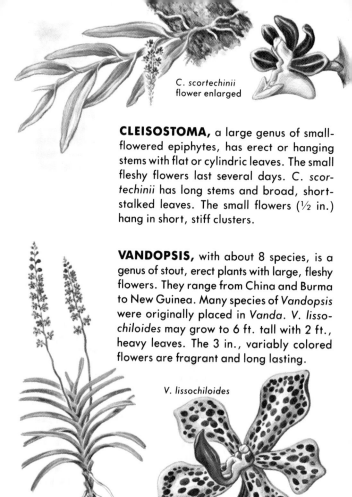

C. scortechinii
flower enlarged

CLEISOSTOMA, a large genus of small-flowered epiphytes, has erect or hanging stems with flat or cylindric leaves. The small fleshy flowers last several days. C. *scortechinii* has long stems and broad, short-stalked leaves. The small flowers (½ in.) hang in short, stiff clusters.

VANDOPSIS, with about 8 species, is a genus of stout, erect plants with large, fleshy flowers. They range from China and Burma to New Guinea. Many species of *Vandopsis* were originally placed in *Vanda*. V. *lissochiloides* may grow to 6 ft. tall with 2 ft., heavy leaves. The 3 in., variably colored flowers are fragrant and long lasting.

V. lissochiloides

TRICHOGLOTTIS, with about 60 species of epiphytic, vinelike orchids from Asia, Indonesia, and Polynesia, is characterized by a tongue-shaped plate at the back of the lip, horns on the column, and a complicated lip mid-lobe.

TRICHOGLOTTIS FASCIATA is a climbing plant with leathery leaves. The 2 in., brown-banded, yellow flowers are waxy, fragrant, and long lasting. They are produced 2-4 on a raceme. The brown-spotted, white lip is fuzzy and with the side lobes forms a cross.

TRICHOGLOTTIS PHILIPPI-NENSIS, usually erect with short recurving leaves, has solitary or paired flowers. The sepals and petals vary from reddish tan to almost black-purple. The dark-maroon species, *T. brachiata,* is sometimes known as the Black Orchid.

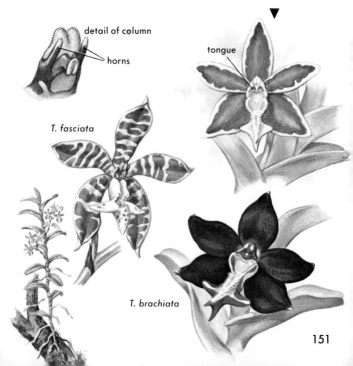

detail of column

horns

tongue

T. fasciata

T. brachiata

151

ANGRAECUM, largely restricted to Africa and islands of the Indian Ocean, includes over 200 species which vary vegetatively, but many are like *Vanda*. The flowers are nearly all white or greenish white. Many are starlike, and all have a medium to long, slender spur.

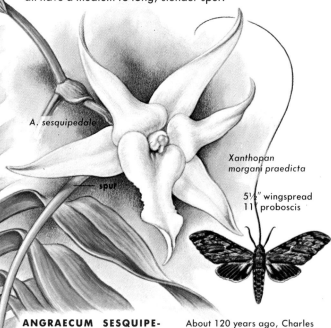

A. sesquipedale

spur

Xanthopan morgani praedicta

5½" wingspread
11" proboscis

ANGRAECUM SESQUIPE-DALE, known as the Star-of-Bethlehem Orchid, has star-shaped, ivory-white flowers that bloom around Christmas. Two to four fragrant waxy flowers, up to 7 in. across, seem to glow against the background of closely arranged leaves. Their barely noticeable nectar tube is a whitish-green spur, almost 1 ft. long.

About 120 years ago, Charles Darwin, studying the fertilization of orchids by insects, predicted that in Madagascar there must be a moth with a 10-11 in. proboscis capable of reaching the nectar at the bottom of the tube and fertilizing this flower. Many years later such a moth—the night-flying *Xanthopan morgani praedicta*—was found.

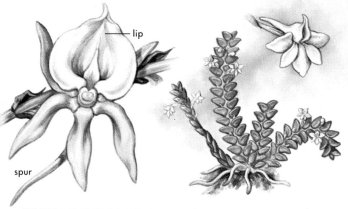

ANGRAECUM EBURNEUM, with a growth like *Vanda,* may reach 6 ft. tall. It has 2 ft. leathery leaves with an arching, lateral raceme, bearing many 3 in. greenish-white, inverted flowers, each with a 3-4 in. spur.

ANGRAECUM EICHLERIANUM climbs tree trunks, its leaves flattened against the bark. The 1-3 whitish flowers are about 3 in. across with a 2 in. spur.

MYSTACIDIUM DISTICHUM, also called *Angraecum distichum,* is a dwarf species with entangled masses of clustered stems to 6 in. long, overlapping glossy-green leaves, and ¼ in. white flowers.

ANGRAECUM SCOTTIANUM has branched cylindric stems to 2 ft. high with terete leaves. The whitish flowers are up to 2 in. across with a 4-5 in. spur.

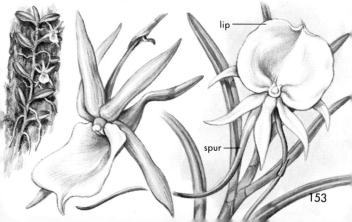

153

AERANTHES, a genus of about 30 species from Madagascar and adjacent islands, has very short stems, a few large leathery leaves, and basal inflorescences. A *grandiflora* has 12 in. leaves and pendent racemes with 1-2 fragrant, long-lasting flowers up to 8 in. across.

A. grandiflora

bud

A. luteo-alba var. rhodosticta

AERANGIS, with about 50 species from tropical Africa, Madagascar, and nearby islands, has white, star-shaped flowers with long spurs. *A. luteo-alba* var. *rhodosticta*, with up to eight, 6 in. leaves spreading in one plane, bears 6-25 flowers in 2 rows in a broad, flat raceme.

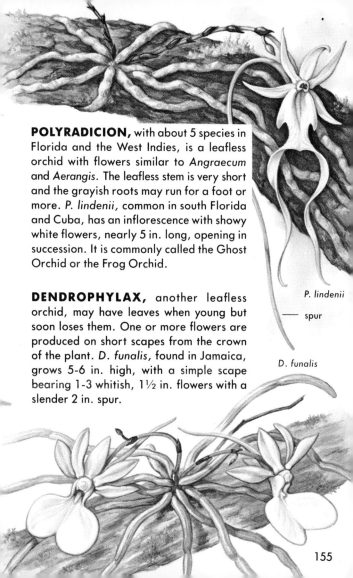

POLYRADICION, with about 5 species in Florida and the West Indies, is a leafless orchid with flowers similar to *Angraecum* and *Aerangis*. The leafless stem is very short and the grayish roots may run for a foot or more. *P. lindenii,* common in south Florida and Cuba, has an inflorescence with showy white flowers, nearly 5 in. long, opening in succession. It is commonly called the Ghost Orchid or the Frog Orchid.

DENDROPHYLAX, another leafless orchid, may have leaves when young but soon loses them. One or more flowers are produced on short scapes from the crown of the plant. *D. funalis,* found in Jamaica, grows 5-6 in. high, with a simple scape bearing 1-3 whitish, 1½ in. flowers with a slender 2 in. spur.

P. lindenii

— spur

D. funalis

THE AMERICAN ORCHID SOCIETY

The American Orchid Society is a non-profit educational and horticultural organization whose basic aims are to stimulate and develop interest in the culture, improvement, use, study, and conservation of orchids, and whose primary activity is the dissemination of information and assistance to achieve these aims.

The Society was formed in 1921 by amateur, private, and commercial growers, with membership including prominent orchidists throughout the world.

In 1932, the Society began its quarterly *Bulletin* which was expanded to a monthly periodical in 1940.

After incorporation in 1948, management of the Society was placed in the hands of a paid Executive Director. From less than 100 members in 1921, the Society has grown to a membership of over 23,000.

While the Society's main activity is the monthly *AOS Bulletin,* with over 100 pages of informative articles and frequent color features, the Society also offers the *Awards Quarterly, Lindleyana* (a renowned scientific journal), a yearbook, and books and videocassettes on orchid culture. American Orchid Society judging is regularly held at regional centers and orchid shows throughout the United States, Canada, and Latin America.

Because of the increasing interest in orchids, the American Orchid Society has fostered the development of local orchid societies, of which there are now almost 500 affiliated with the parent organization throughout the world.

The central office of the American Orchid Society is located at 6000 South Olive Avenue, West Palm Beach, Florida 33405. A clearinghouse for orchid information, the staff welcomes all inquiries, whether for advice or concerning membership (telephone: 407-585-8666).

INDEX

157

159

B C D E F G